Ken Smukler is a nationally recognized political consultant who designed and executed groundbreaking technologies for the media coverage of U.S. presidential elections from 2004 through 2016 for NBC (2004), CNN (2008), RadioOne (2012), and ViceNews (2016).

In 2016, he began to expose a network of hate-based emails circulating among law enforcement agencies at the federal, state, and local levels; a network that included state judges, public defenders, and the criminal defense bar in Pennsylvania – a scandal that became known as "Porngate."

In 2017, Mr. Smukler was indicted by federal prosecutors for alleged violations of the Federal Election Campaign Act for election activity conducted in 2012 and 2014. He was subsequently convicted on 7 of eleven counts.

Mr. Smukler was sentenced to serve 18 months in the Fairton Federal Correctional Institution where he served 310 days, which is where this part of our story begins...and ends.

To my wife, Shelly; and daughters Lucille, Phoebe, and Camille.

Ken Smukler

THE JAILBIRD DIET

Losing 100 Pounds and Finding
Myself Behind Bars

AUSTIN MACAULEY PUBLISHERS™

LONDON • CAMBRIDGE • NEW YORK • SHARJAH

Ordering Information
Quantity sales: Special discounts are available on quantity purchases by corporations, associations, and others. For details, contact the publisher at the address below.

Publisher's Cataloging-in-Publication data
Smukler, Ken
The JailBird Diet

ISBN 9781685624569 (Paperback)
ISBN 9781685624576 (Hardback)
ISBN 9781685624583 (ePub e-book)

Library of Congress Control Number: 2023904560

www.austinmacauley.com/us

First Published 2023
Austin Macauley Publishers LLC
40 Wall Street,33rd Floor, Suite 3302
New York, NY 10005
USA

mail-usa@austinmacauley.com
+1 (646) 5125767

When I was first incarcerated, it was not in the Fairton Federal Correctional facility in Millville, New Jersey. No, my first time behind bars was in a holding cell in the William Green Federal Office Building in Philadelphia.

For a period of three hours, I sat with a group of 10 men, most of whom were currently incarcerated in a federal facility awaiting arraignment on additional charges. The conversation among these inmates (I was silent) ranged from 76ers basketball, rap lyrics, the former District Attorney (now locked up in the local federal detention facility) and all aspects of life in prison. At the time, this was a world I believed I would never really know, confident that my future did not include a 300+ day stay in a federal penitentiary. So I did not pay much attention to the banter save for one piece of advice given from one inmate to one soon-to-be-inmate: No matter how long you are down, if you have family and friends who support you on the outside, you can make it through.

This book could not have been written without my family and friends who supported me each and every day of the 310 days I spent in federal prison.

There was another support group for whom no amount of acknowledgment can ever repay – the men I served time with at the Fairton Correctional Institute from June 18, 2019 to April 29, 2020.

You will see some of these men in the pages to come. Their names have been changed, though, should any of them ever read this book, I have no doubt that they will recognize themselves.

From the first day that I entered the housing unit at FCI and I was greeted at my bunk with hand-outs of soap, a toothbrush, sneakers, and a radio, to the last day I left the Medium Security facility to their cheering from the satellite camp across the parking lot, they made my life inside a life worth living; they created the framework for the world in which I could lose 100 pounds and find myself behind bars.

Table of Contents

Author's Note

The origin of the word jailbird – or rather gaol bird – can be traced back at least to medieval England, where convicts were oftentimes locked in iron cages that were then suspended several feet above the ground. Visible to passersby, it was strongly suggested by those in charge that the passersby refer to them as jailbirds since the suspended iron cages somewhat resembled bird cages.

The Jailbird Diet is a cage. Place your mind and body within it and become, as I did, reborn.

I am the most unlikely of diet book authors. I have never read a diet book nor followed a diet regimen. I only engaged in one sustained period of weight loss and that was as part of a wager I placed with a congressman for whom I worked. He started at 305 pounds, I at 300 pounds and we both ended up six months later at 250. He won the bet which was for a dinner that we never had. That was in 2011.

The path that led me to writing this book was not a path I chose. It began nearly five years ago, on May 13, 2017 when three FBI agents knocked at my door at 7:00 A.M. (followed by ten more conducting a room-by-room search of my house) to interrogate me for five hours about political campaigns I had overseen in 2014 and 2012. This interrogation led to my 2018 indictment on 11 counts of violating federal campaign finance laws.

The thrust of my defense was that I was being vindictively prosecuted for my efforts in exposing the participation of FBI agents and U.S. attorneys in a network of racist, misogynistic, homophobic, and anti-Muslim emails that came to be referred to in the press as "Porngate." In pre-trial motions, I argued that federal prosecutors had weaponized campaign finance laws to criminalize behavior never before found criminal in retaliation for my efforts to take them down.

The jury never heard any of this.

In part, the federal prosecutors trying the case against me were right. I did try to take them down. And I paid for it. They sought to put me in jail for six years, the judge sentenced me to 18 months.

I self-surrendered at the Fairton Correction Institute in Millville, New Jersey on Monday June 17, 2019 which is where our story begins.

Foreword

I have been in this room before. I have sat on this stainless-steel bench before. Four walls of cinderblock 13 feet high painted chalk white with a royal navy-blue trimming at the bottom. The blue matches the door to my right – steel with a small square window of glass and a slot below it for meals.

To the door's left is a window – four boxes of reinforced glass like those in a storybook village but these are framed by steel and have six evenly spaced metal bars running up and down them. Through the window, I can see guards walking back and forth. Just another Thursday morning for them. Not for me.

The walls all scream warnings in pencil scribbled on the pock-marked cinderblock. Beware of this rat. Warning: he's a snitch…there's a ChoMo inside the fence. And they scream defiance – Newark Gangland, Camden, NJ, Fee401, >>>Blue>>>.

A silver dome-like a mylar balloon is propped in the upper corner of the room to my left – the unblinking eye of some alien being – looking down over my shoulder from its perch.

I see a pencil jammed between the steel bench and the wall. I try to pull it out but it is wedged too tight. What would I write? What would be my one statement to all those who enter these walls? Abandon hope all ye who enter here?

But today I am not entering. Today I am heading outside the wire, leaving the rats and snitches, ChoMos and gangbangers, behind. Leaving. Finally.

I know that she is in the next room.

As I said, I have been in this room before. The wall across from where I sit that separates the two of us has its own storybook window. I peer through it but all I can see is gurneys, wheelchairs, and a desk with a computer. The screen saver flashes a map of America with colored dots spread out across the

13

states and these words in red caps across the screen – WE FACE WHAT YOU FEAR. I know she is in there.

I met her sister ten months ago. I spent each morning of those ten months looking into her sister's eye. Now I know I will never see her sister again. So I wait. And hope. Hope that I will be allowed to see this sister – one last reminder of who I was and what I came here for; one last reminder before I cross over the barbed wire and leave this place for good, or bad, or whatever, I do not care. Just leaving is good enough for now.

I desperately need to look her in the eye and feel what I felt each morning when I looked into her sister's eye. One last look will complete my journey. Tell me – reaffirm for me – that the journey was somehow worth the price I had paid to embark upon it; that the pledge I made to family and friends and to myself was a pledge I kept. Just one last look was all I asked.

The royal blue door opens. It is time. I ask the man with the keys if he could spare one moment to open the door to the room next door. Men with keys are an unpredictable lot. I have found this out the hard way. They are like big cats in a poor-man's traveling circus – one day they cuddle with you the next day they maul your face off. But this man with the keys wants me to know he is one of the good ones. He meets my request with a casual "sure no problem" and I am relieved – my journey I now know will end as it should.

I enter the room. The man with the keys stands right behind me – still facing one to fear I suppose. I go directly to her, stand before her, kick my sneakers off, and begin to undress; sweatpants, sweatshirt, T-shirt all drop to the floor at her feet. I sense the man with the keys is getting nervous, I tell him I will go no further.

Now I am standing before her as I stood before her sister. She has the same tattoo of a cardinal on her upper right cheek yet she is different. No two sisters are alike. When I touch her, she is more jittery than her sister, her eye closes shut as though she is focusing on what to say – both she and her sister were born that way.

I touch her again and her eye begins to flutter. Now it opens like she has seen a ghost. Then it narrows into a dead stare. She is ready to tell me the truth and I am ready for it.

The truth. 185. And I am free.

Note:

Detecto's physician scale model 439 features a die-cast beam that can be easily read from either side. Detecto was founded in 1900 in Brooklyn, New York by three immigrants, the Jacobs brothers, and went onto become a leading manufacturer of Bakers' Dough scales, Butcher's scales, hanging scales and portion scales.

In 1950, William H. Perry starts Cardinal Scale in his garage located in his hometown of Webb City, Missouri. In 1981, Cardinal Scale acquired Detecto becoming a leader in healthcare scales.

And that is how she got her cardinal tattoo.

Chapter 1
Into the Woods:
What a Nineteenth Century
Transcendentalist
Taught Me About Twenty-First Century
Weight Loss

"I went to the woods because I wished to live deliberately, to front only the essential facts of life, and see if I could not learn what it had to teach, and not, when I came to die, discover that I had not lived. I did not wish to live what was not life, living is so dear; nor did I wish to practice resignation, unless it was quite necessary. I wanted to live deep and suck out all the marrow life, to live so sturdily and Spartan-like as to put route all that was not life, to cut a broad swath and shave close, to drive life into a corner, and reduce it to its lowest terms, and, if proved to be mean, why then to get the whole and genuine meanness it, and publish its meanness of it, and the world; or if it were sublime, to know it by experience, and be able to give it a true account of it in my next excursion."
Walden, p. 51

Henry David Thoreau did not walk into the woods to lose weight. By all accounts, he was not obese. As a victim of tuberculosis at an early age, he most likely had more trouble keeping weight on than taking it off. He did not write the classic nineteenth century transcendentalist work, *Walden*, to help his readers lose weight. He seemed more interested in the length of his nose than the breadth of his waistline.

There is an old joke among Thoreauvians (I kid you not, that is what fans of the nineteenth century Transcendentalist are called) that Thoreau spent half his life at Walden Pond and the other half in jail. Henry David Thoreau spent, in fact, two years, two months, and two days in the wilderness of Walden Pond outside Concord Massachusetts (July 4, 1845 – September 6, 1847). His experience in the woods is memorialized in "*Walden.*" He spent one day, July 23, 1846, in prison for refusing to pay a poll tax on the grounds that it was funding the Mexican American War which he opposed. His jail time was cut short due to the payment of his tax obligations by an unknown benefactor. The experience in the Concord township jail was memorialized in his treatise, "*Civil Disobedience.*"

Walden's two years in the woods were spent outside Concord Massachusetts. He lived in a small log cabin that he built on the property of his good friend, mentor, and benefactor, the nineteenth century Transcendentalist, Ralph Waldo Emerson. On June 17, 2019, I went into the woods of Fairton Correctional Institute outside Milleville New Jersey – 340 miles south of Walden Pond and 174 years later.

I surrendered myself to the woods. I did not pick the time and place, a federal judge did that for me. I had no goal other than to survive. I answered to uniforms every day. I came in as a number – 76315-066 – and left 308 days later as that number.

Though Waldon Pond and the satellite camp at Fairton are separated in time and space, the principles guiding Thoreau's journey into the woods are the very principles that guided my weight loss journey; the principles that provided me the structure and foundation upon which I set out to live my life away from family, friends, and the rest of the free world.

These pages lay out the weight loss plan I structured for myself from the first day I entered my woods to the day I returned to the free world. To successfully carry out this weight loss plan does not require the recording of calories though you will be recording what you eat every meal of every day through the journey. As Thoreau recorded what he planted and the costs of every item used to build his house and maintain his diet, you will record your journey.

The Jailbird Diet does not require you to choose certain foods over others though it does require you to diligently restrict the amount of junk in your lifestyle; it does not tell you the super foods you should eat to maintain a healthy diet while losing weight but it does tell you the super "foods" you should incorporate into your life to sustain short-term significant weight loss.

The Jailbird Diet does not focus on the pyramid of food groups but on the myriad of day-to-day choices beyond food that will predict whether or not you have what it takes to sustain a short-term weight loss program.

Thoreau left society and placed his entire mind and body into the wilderness; he wanted for nothing that he had left behind in the town of Concord. In fact, he disdained much of what he found there: the commerce, the trappings, the gossip, the petty, the morally reprehensible, what he called "most of the luxuries, and many of the so-called comforts of life" – what I call the junk – all of it to be left behind to live in an exalted state within the woods.

"I learned this, at least, by my experiment: that if one advances confidently in the direction of his dreams, and endeavors to live the life which he has imagined, he will meet with a success unexpected in common hours. He will put some things behind, will pass an invisible boundary...In proportion as he simplifies his life, the laws of the universe will appear less complex and solitude will not be solitude...If you have built castles in the air, your work need not be lost, that is where they should be. Now put the foundations under them."

Walden, p. 52

If there is any secret to my diet success, it is this: Simplify your life by limiting the amount of junk you consume – in all of its non-eating aspects – and you will trigger your brain and body to not desire junk in your food diet and, in so doing, lose weight. Replace the junk in your day-to-day life choices with healthy day-to-day experiences that challenge your mind and body and hunger will dissipate even as your body confronts a highly restrictive diet. Place yourself within a solitude that rejects junk, in all of its non-food forms, replace that junk with super "foods" that engage your mind, body and soul, and you will succeed.

The Jailbird Diet is driven by lifestyle choices rather than food choices.

Thoreau achieved this lifestyle by walking into the woods and staying there for two years. I did it through a forced incarceration over ten months. But you need not physically remove yourself from society to clear out your junk files. Thoreau recognized this.

"A man thinking or working is always alone, let him be where he will. Solitude is not measured by the miles of space that intervene between a man and his fellows. The really diligent student in one of the crowded hives of Cambridge College is as solitary as a dervish in the desert."
Walden p. 75

Solitude can be achieved anywhere. Solitude is a state of mind.

His approach to the junk of the nineteenth century informed my approach to the junk of the twenty-first century each and every day I was incarcerated. It was this approach that guided my mind toward a rigorous discipline of junk removal that allowed me to sustain my weight loss program.

I began to treat everything that I consumed, beyond what one traditionally associates with weight gain, namely food, as part of my diet. Junk food was not simply what I put into my mouth, it was what I put into my mind: junk food was not simply potato chips and candy, strombolis and pizza, but junk news, junk books and magazines, junk television, junk Internet, junk relationships, junk business, junk science, junk communication, junk photos, and junk videos.

"What is the pill which will keep us well, serene, contented? For my panacea, instead of one of those quack vials of a mixture dipped from Acheron and the Dead Sea...let me have a draught of undiluted morning air. Morning air! If men will not drink of this at the fountainhead of the day, why, then, we must even bottle up some and sell it in the shops, for the benefit of those who have lost their subscription ticket to morning time in this world."
Walden, p. 77

When Thoureau speaks of breaths of fresh air as an elixir, he is not simply speaking to the air he breathes but to everything else he no longer breathes. He called the junk *"not only not indispensable but positive hindrances to the elevation of mankind. With respect to luxuries and comforts, the wisest have ever lived a more simple and meager life than the poor."*

We all accept as Gospel that removing junk food from one's diet is a necessary prerequisite to short-term weight loss. It is time we accept that removing junk media, junk internet, junk television, and junk relationships is equally necessary to achieving weight loss success. I came to realize that these

19

non-food junk "foods" were hunger triggers for me; by removing them, I took hunger off the table. My body and mind no longer recognized and reacted to hunger signals and began to accept the long-term reduction in my food and caloric intake. That this happens as a fact I know because for ten months I lived it.

What I don't know is the science that makes this diet work.

If you haven't figured out by now, my weight loss regimen was predicated on no more than an idiot's understanding of the science around weight loss. Since returning to the free world, I have found no scientific evidence or theories that support my contention that junk-based daily life choices drive hunger which drives caloric consumption and causes diets to fail. But I am no less convinced that removing junk-based life choices from your daily diet leads to sustained weight loss than I am in the simple mathematical formula – burning more calories than one consumes on a daily basis equals consistent weight loss – that forms the basic science of weight loss. I have no doubt there is solid science behind the steps I took to drop 100 pounds in ten months, I just don't think dieting has been studied in this way.

I have seen studies that speak to the brain and hunger; studies that identify signals from the brain's hypothalamus as being as important to hunger cessation as signals from your stomach. But these studies speak to the brain dealing with food and appetite directly. I am speaking to re-tooling your brain in ways that have nothing to do with food.

At the end of this book, I present what may be the scientific underpinnings of this diet. This was done by nothing more than online searches when I returned to the free world (no intent for the incarcerated). For those looking for the science behind the diet, I hope this provides a starting place for your research.

For those more interested in the stories behind the diet, I hope they illuminate the one overriding principle that I stole from Thoreau and his experience in the woods around Walden Pond: Sustained short-term weight loss can be attained by placing your mind in a position to burn more calories than you consume 'in any environment' regardless of the food choices that you make on a daily basis.

You do not need to go to a fat camp or spa to put yourself in a position to lose weight. You do not need pre-packaged foods or a number system. You do not need pills or medication. And you do not need to starve yourself. You do need, however, to prepare your mind and body for such a journey.

It was not the food choices that I made in prison that drove my weight down; it was how I decided I would live my life in prison that allowed me to make the food choices that ultimately led to significant sustained weight loss. It was everything that happened outside of the time I was sitting at a table in the chow hall that caused my drop in weight; my new eating habits were merely the symptoms brought on by a vigorous adherence to a daily mental and physical regime that removed food from the equation. As I came to understand in the early days of my incarceration, if the regimen removes hunger from the equation, food becomes fuel to be burned and nothing more.

Can Thoreau's approach to living be adapted to the pursuit of significant weight loss? Can an overarching life-changing plan to simplify your existence on this earth be the very plan that can successfully launch a short-term large-scale weight loss program? One that could melt 25–30% of your body weight away? One that could result in your losing 100 pounds in less than a year?

Can limited caloric intake be sustained over the short-term not because you willed it or pilled it but because you didn't focus on the food part of dieting but focused on everything else in your life except for the food? Can the key to short-term weight loss have nothing to do with your food choices and everything to do with all the choices you make when you are not eating?

Can hunger be satiated, not by drugs or sheer will power, but by fundamentally simplifying your lifestyle? If you remove all that junks up your life, can you then more easily remove the desire for food that junks up your diet?

Yes. Yes. Yes. Yes. Yes. And yes.

The Jailbird Diet establishes the ground rules that puts your mind and body in a position to remove hunger and the desire to eat more calories than you burn on a daily basis. While the formula for weight loss is a simple one, creating the environment within which to adhere to this formula is anything but easy. For me, it required a sustained physical, mental, and emotional solitude that is very difficult to achieve in the free world. But if you get your mind and body there, weight loss will follow. That is the only promise I make to you, the reader.

Part I
Setting the Table

Chapter 2
Shock and Awful

I could not but smile to see how industriously they locked the door on my meditations, which followed them out again without let or hindrance, and they were really all that was dangerous. As they could not reach me, they resolved to punish my body; just as boys, if they cannot come at some person against whom they have a spite, will abuse his dog...Thus the State never intentionally confronts a man's sense, but only his body, his senses.
  Civil Disobedience, p. 10

Thoreau built a small cabin in the woods, spent his days outside raising crops and walking in the woods, and spent his nights reading and writing. Incarceration in a federal prison camp allows for a very similar existence if you set yourself to the task of living as simply as possible.

A bunk to sleep in, a place to walk in the woods, nights spent reading and writing – these defined my experience in federal custody: an environment totally unlike that in which I was raised, worked, and lived for the 58 years prior to June 17, 2019; an environment only those in federal custody can understand; an environment I call, "Shock and Awful."

As I write this, I am sitting in a 7' × 9' cell looking out a barred window across a prison yard crisscrossed by razor wire. You want to find a really good place to get your head around a long-term weight loss plan? This is the place. But this is not where I started. This is where my journey will end. I move my chair to face the window. In the far-left corner of my sightline over and above the razor wires I can just make out the building where my journey began ten months ago – R and D, Receipt and Discharge.

R and D is the perfect orientation for a prisoner entering a federal correctional institution as a self-surrender (e.g. not dropping down from a higher security facility as the majority of inmates did at my camp); its very name triggers your self-identification as something less than human.

The first interaction with a prison guard is the take-off-all-your-clothes strip search – pull your package up for the full frontal, bend over for the anal cavity peak on the back side. Thus begins the transformation from human being with a soul to institutional package with a SKU number and barcode: A number and code that is never to leave you; one that is entered when you talk on the phone, send email, receive snail mail, when you are called to the office and when you go to see visitors.

Entering prison is, in many ways, like entering a public high school in the 1960s and 70s: cinderblock walls, linoleum floors, industrial lighting, industrial cleaning, all metal and plastic everywhere you go, everything you touch, all that you smell, see, hear, taste…all concrete, metal, plastic, and industrial cleaning products.

This artificial industrialized sensation overload plays with your mind. Noises that may have caused you to jump back on the outside become as inconsequential as the purr of a kitten. You never walk around barefoot, indoor, outdoor, certainly not in the bathroom or shower. There is no real measure of ambient light streaming into any indoor area – not where you eat or where you sleep. The indoor light hits you from 35 feet above like the light of an oncoming train. The forced air cools both housing unit and chow hall to temperatures well below what your home thermostat would call for even on the hottest of summer nights. It was not uncommon to see men in full sweats, scarf and knit hat watching television in the chow hall in the middle of July. I was told that the frosty clime was to keep flies and insects to a minimum just as the din of the industrial fan running 24/7 in the bathroom was to keep sounds and smells to a minimum and, as everything in BOP [Bureau of Prisons]-land happens for a reason no matter how illogical or inane (see the Coronavirus response later on in Chapter X. Pandemic), I guess these measures worked.

It's not simply that your world is thrown upside down when you enter a federal prison. It's that your world in every sensation becomes louder, brighter, colder, rougher, smellier. All of your senses bombarded, putting your whole body on edge.

Guys sleeping with their CPAP machines disconnected creating a cascade of snoregasms; 60 bunk beds lined up in a warehouse in which the men slept, as Joseph Conrad described in *Heart of Darkness*, "with all the taps turned on."

In the chow hall, hard plastic cups, sporks, discolored plastic dining trays like over-sized Swanson Hungry Man TV dinners. I came to crave silverware, china, glassware almost as much as I craved a lobster roll or grilled fish. One of my favorite campers, let's call him Jaws for the metalware in his mouth, once turned to me on chow line holding his brown plastic cup up to his eyes, saying dreamily, "I haven't had water in a real glass in ten years."

In the bathroom, if the industrial fan and hand blowers aren't assaulting your auditory senses, the scalding water that hits your body from the showers will – it leaves you breathless.

[Aside: This is a story that will tell you all you need to know about the Catch-22 that is the BOP – or as one administrator called it, the BOP – Broken On Purpose. When I got to camp, the shower stalls were equipped with a metal button connected to the waterline leading to the shower head – this button you would push to maintain water pressure like the morphine drip button in a post-op hospital bed. There was no regulator for hot or cold. This led to moments when the water temperature would spike to scalding without warning. I was told that the BOP implemented this system in order to economize on water usage and not over tax the hot water heater. The campers, as they routinely do, figured out a workaround for the scalding: Turn all the sinks' hot water on full blast and leave all ten running while you take your shower. During the time I was at camp, prior to the switching out of the shower pump nozzle for the standard hot-cold regulators five months into my stay, the sinks were constantly pouring out hot water throughout the day and night. Whatever savings the pump nozzles created in the showers were going down the drain so to speak in the sinks every day and night.]

Your sense of space also takes a hit. I am sleeping two feet above another human being, two feet next to two others with a corridor of human traffic flowing by the other side of my bed at all hours, day and night. The sound of walkie talkies, boots, jangling keys, and the idle conversation of guards hits at regular intervals of the night at 12:30, 3:30 and 5:00 A.M. as the cops make their rounds through the housing unit. If you choose to hang out at your bunk, you will be doing so with someone talking, eating, sleeping, snoring or farting within arm's length at all times.

A curious de-socialization occurs when you are forced to bunk with 119 men in a common room. The idea that voices should be lowered while the men are sleeping is as foreign as the touch of a woman in the housing unit.

At first, I thought it was the cops (what we call prison guards) putting the penal in penal institution by keeping their walkie talkies up at full volume or conversing with one another at equally full volume as they patrolled the unit during lights out period (11:00 P.M. to 6:00 A.M.). I quickly came to understand that the campers did not abide by the social convention of letting sleeping dogs lie either. Campers coming in from the chow hall in the middle of the night (if you were watching television in the chow hall past lights out at 11:00 P.M., you were required to be back at your bed for count at 12:30 A.M. and 3:30 A.M.) would regularly converse with one another as though it were the middle of the day. And I heard everything. My assigned bunk was in the heart of Times Square – the intersection of the main walkway from the double doors leading in from the bathroom and chow hall to the cop station – the equivalent of the librarian's desk at the public library – where a cop would sit throughout the day and some of the night.

If the constant assault on all senses did not place my body onto a wartime footing, the precariousness of my health and well-being did.

I came to camp with nerve damage radiating down my left leg leaving me with a dropped left foot. I came armed with two doctors' notes warning of the hazards of my attempting to mount the upper berth of a bunk bed (I had been alerted to the existence of bunk beds at the camp by a former inmate). Upon presentation of these notes to the Camp Counselor at R and D, I was immediately assigned to bunk 24 U – U standing for Upper. So much for doctors' notes.

This left me with only one choice: attempt the ascent of my upper bunk only one time each day and do so when the lights were out. I was not about to have other inmates see how ridiculous the sight of a morbidly obese middle-aged man with the use of one leg mounting a bunk bed could be.

So when the housing unit lights were turned out at 11:00 P.M., I took my night-reading light in hand, stacked my plastic chair (every bunk bed gets two – mine was the 24 U chair) on top of my bunky's at the foot of the bed at the base of the 4-rung ladder to the upper berth. I put my pillow on the stacked chairs then placed my dead foot on the pillow platform launching my right knee over the upper berth bed frame and driving it onto the mattress. Once the knee was set, with my right hand, I grabbed the metal rail at the foot of the upper berth and hurled the right side of my body onto the bed the damaged left leg then naturally followed upwards to the bed and I ended up on my back.

The trick was being careful not to launch myself over the far side onto the linoleum covered concrete floor five feet below.

Unintended airborne dismounts are not that uncommon – two occurred during my stay: Hans Gruber (named after the Alan Rickman-portrayed Die Hard villain because he was, you guessed it, German) routinely stayed up all night drinking Diet Coke's on his bed only to fall one night leaving him with a soft cast on his left wrist for the remainder of his stay; Big I – a bald hulking tattoo gallery of an inmate – took a spill only to be met with the typical camper response the next day: "Hey, Big I, heard you tried to fly last night."

As precarious as the mounting was for me, the descent was far scarier. Five feet off the ground may not seem that far to you, but looking down on it each morning placed me at considerable unease. To deal with this, I commissioned, let's call him Le Carre (he was truly Tinker, Tailor, Soldier, Spy – a camper of considerable talent ranging from needle and thread to plumbing to chemistry now serving or what inmates call "down" 20 years for cooking meth), to fashion me an oversized pillow. Each morning I would place it vertically upon the stacked chairs at the foot of the bunk bed. I then proceeded to wedge my dead left foot as far down into the pillow as it could go making sure to maintain balance lest I tip the chairs backward and go sprawling to the linoleum. I then lowered my right foot (the good one) onto the frame of the lower bunk bed next to mine (as the camper in this bed worked down the service road requiring him to be up and out by 6:30 A.M. each weekday morning I would wait till he departed to begin my dismount). Now straddling the open space between our beds perched on bed and pillow while holding the rail at the foot of my upper berth bed frame in my clenched fist. Then with one move I took my free right arm and lunged to the upper berth frame of the neighboring bunkbed grabbing it (the camper in the upper berth was in bed but out of it doing what was referred to as "drug time" – staying up all night then crashing just before the 5:00 A.M. count and sleeping through the day), at the same time pivoting my dead left foot on the pillow to spin myself around allowing myself to lower my good right foot from the neighboring lower bunk to the floor and complete the maneuver by lowering my dead left foot from the pillow to the floor; but making sure, in so doing, I did not knock the pillow to floor to pick up God knows what microorganisms were lurking there.

This ritual repeated itself each night and morning for the first six weeks of my stay – the day that I received the equivalent of the Willie Wonka Golden

Ticket – the lower bunk pass. When my bunky decided to move out of Times Square to the suburbs, I moved down to the lower bunk where I remained till the day I packed out.

Of course, my precarious perch triggered other angst-ridden moments. When mounting and dismounting can only be attempted twice during a 24-hour period, one has to remove any notion that relieving oneself during the night is an option. As a 58-year-old male, I was used to a regular one-time nightly run and occasional two-time dashes. This was now out of the question. My solution to this predicament was two-fold.

First, stop consuming any beverage at first, after 7:00 P.M., then after 3:00 P.M., finally after noon. The only water that would breach my gums after these hours was the bathroom tap to brush my teeth.

Second, body positioning. When you sleep on a two-inch foam mattress covered in plastic on a metal frame that barely extends beyond your shoulders and hips, and you are on an upper bunk in constant fear of flight, you become intimately familiar with body positioning. Lying on my right side would create the quickest "I-gotta-go" sensation only abated temporarily by bringing my knees to my chest placing myself into a fetal position. To ameliorate the sensation entirely, I would move to my left side and assume the high jumper pose – left leg extended completely and jammed into the far corner of the bed frame; right knee brought as far up to my chest as possible. Aaaaah! When this finally failed, the last measure was to lie entirely upon my back and hold the hose until the morning wake-up call which happened generally at 5:45 every morning.

5:45 A.M.: "Pill Line!" "Pill Line!"

I can still here the cry as I write this (there is no pill line in solitary as they bring the pills to each cell).

[Aside: While the political conversation in America at times has focused considerable debate upon the issue of healthcare as a right of all Americans, there is one population of Americans for which healthcare has been, in fact, a right for decades – the American prisoner. Politicians would be wise to look at the prison healthcare system if they truly want to see what healthcare as a right means. Twice a day, once at 5:45 A.M. and next at 3:45 P.M., the health office door situated in the hallway between chow hall and housing unit would be opened for a queue of prisoners to form to receive their daily medication. I was told that this is primarily for the dispensation of insulin and blood pressure medication. Roughly 20% of the campers, primarily the older white population, would line up.]

6:00 A.M.: "Pill Line!" "Pill Line"

As this cry was launched from the cop station, which in Times Square could be reached in one arm's length from my bed, my ears were the first to receive the onslaught. Thus began each day of sensory sadism institutionalized by the BOP. There were less benign attacks on my peace of mind to deal with as well – the constant fear that I was in the wrong place, doing the wrong thing, sitting in the wrong seat, looking the wrong way, wearing the wrong stuff – rules written and unwritten and too easily broken by one like myself who had not dropped down into the camp from a higher security institution.

In the first few days, I broke many: going outside the housing unit before the count was cleared, wearing my baseball cap backward in the housing unit (disrespectful to gang bangers who sartorially signify their status this way); using a shower dedicated to another camper's time slot; not falling into the chow line correctly (when two campers in two lines are merging to one line, it is critical to make eye contact and get acceptance of your going first; failure to do so infringes upon space boundaries).

The bathroom also has rules. When the rubberized curtain to a toilet stall is closed with a piece of toilet paper hung from the rod upon which the curtain hangs, that stall is being used. No closed curtain, no toilet paper hanging, the stall is fair game. So here I am in week three with my industrial sized toilet paper roll in hand (toilet paper does not come with the stall; the BOP gives each camper one roll the size of those you see in turnpike rest area stalls each month; there are metal prongs in each stall to place these rolls for unfurling). And here is a stall that has no toilet paper hanging from the curtain rod. Fair game, no? I enter it only to find a roll of toilet paper still sitting on its metal rod holder.

And what the fuck are you supposed to do? There is no rule book for this situation. As I am removing this roll to place on a hook by the sink area, a Black camper (I mention race as this was the first interaction I had with any Black inmate other than my bunky since I arrived), we'll call him Max, gets in my face and does one of these: "Your new to prison so I'm gonna let you off this time but NEVER TOUCH ANOTHER INMATES'S STUFF."

31

Beyond the environmental angst and the unwritten rules and regs panic, the greatest anxiety was caused by the erratic and mercurial nature of the cops.

Many years ago, I was headed to London with a buddy of mine when we were stopped at the TSA check-in point in the international terminal at the Philadelphia Airport. Our bags were pulled out of the screening line where a TSA agent demanded we place all toiletries in a clear plastic bag. Both of us had traveled through airports in the past weeks where neither had confronted such a demand. Letting the TSA agent in on this bit of irony was not helpful and as things began to escalate, a supervisor came over to diffuse the situation with this little tutorial: inconsistency of treatment is a design element of TSA screening meant to keep travelers off guard as to screening procedures.

This planned inconsistency of law enforcement oversight seems to be a guiding mandate of the federal prison system. Rooted in the motto – We Fear What You Face – living in a minimum security prison or camp is still designed to instill the maximum angst and insecurity upon its boarders – at all times: the woman cops – two on two different occasions – who told me to take a step backward when talking to them as though I was breaching some #MeToo spacing requirement; the cop who marched through the housing unit one night with a roll of duct tape opening lockers by each camper's bed and duct taping the apples and oranges he found there (more than one piece of fruit in a locker is considered contraband); the cop taking to the public address system announcing a shakedown of the housing unit (a search this time to remove unauthorized mattresses, pillows, and storage containers) telling us that he was "in a good mood this morning," warning us not to spoil his mood because "you don't want to see what I am like when I get mad."

Then P fell out.

P was my first bunky; a big, young Black man with a ready smile and a quiet, low-key disposition. I first found out he had seizures when I started working in food service. P was a "linebacker": the guy who would back up the food line for the servers during lunch and dinner – replacing old serving trays with full ones, making sure there were enough trays and sporks, cleaning the line when the meal was over. One day I needed help bringing boxes off the pull (the regular delivery of food boxes from the food warehouse up the road to the back door of the kitchen). On the regular Thursday pull, all food service workers were expected to report to dock at the back door of the kitchen to help move the boxes into the walk-in freezer, cooler, and dry room. P was exempted from this duty, I was told, due to his seizure condition.

One summer Saturday night, the chow hall – now converted to the TV room – was packed. I was in my seat up against the eastern wall by the juice/water station at the far end of the hall from the double door entrance. Poker games, chess matches, and the black jack table in the computer room just off the chow hall were in full effect. A commotion began at the card table just inside the double doors diagonally across the room to the right from where I sat. Word spread across the room that P had fallen out – the term used for a camper hitting the deck from some ailment. Falling out, as we shall see later is not always an Act of God; this one, however, was. P had simply slumped in his chair while playing cards and was now sprawled onto the floor. Guys were running from the chow hall to the housing unit to get the cop. Everybody is standing and looking toward the corner where P was now propped up and seemingly recovering. The cop comes into the chow hall and tells everyone to clear the room which we do; most of us heading back to our bunks, some loitering in the hallway and bathroom; some staying to administer to P.

Then the lieutenant enters. This is the equivalent of moving from DefCon 5 to DefCon 1; lieutenants rarely showed up in the camp, never on a Saturday night, and nothing ever good happens when they did. This night was no exception.

He comes in yelling. "Everybody at your bunks." "Now." "No talking." When we are all standing at our beds, he asks the cop, "Did you tell these guys to get to their bunks?" The cop lies (he didn't tell us to get to our bunks, he told us to simply clear the chow hall) covering his ass and said he did. This is all the ammo the lieutenant needs.

The lieutenant starts yelling. "You were told to get to your bunks and I find guys in the hallway, in the bathroom. Now who is gonna tell me what happened?"

Silence.

"No one saw what happened? Is that how it's gonna be?"

Silence.

"You think that's gonna help you? Well we're gonna stay here all night if we have until someone talks."

Silence.

33

Then one of the Black shot callers (shot callers are the leaders of each racial grouping), a camper I had never talked to, we'll call him Vibe, comes walking up from the White House – the area of the housing unit partitioned off from the main sleeping area where the roughest Black campers chose to bunk. Vibe now walks between the bunks toward the cop station. The lieutenant yells at him: "Pull your pants up. Take your hat off."

Vibe stops. Pulls his pants up. Takes his hat off.

Lieutenant: "Tell me what happened."

Vibe tells him that P just slumped over, but he was ok once he hit the floor, guys got him water, propped a pillow behind his head and were waiting for the ambulance to show up.

The lieutenant storms out telling us the televisions were gonna be turned off and the chow hall was now off limits for the rest of the night.

When the lieutenant had exited the building, I went up to one of the White shot callers and asked him for advice. If I had actually seen what happened to P, should I have volunteered that information when the lieutenant had asked?

The answer: No. Never.

This is what he told me: Never volunteer information to a cop. In the present situation, or any other for that matter, volunteering can only have negative consequences. Most likely, it could mean taking you, P, and anyone else who was at P's table to the SHU (Special Housing Unit – solitary confinement), keeping you there till Monday (as it was a Saturday night) and only then trying to figure out what happened. You don't get merit badges for volunteering anything. Ever.

[Aside: I now think differently about snitching and the law of the street. I had always thought coming in that the failure to cooperate with the police in the free world was primarily a reaction to the fear of retribution from the criminals you were ratting on. But that is because I had only heard how cops frame the issue. I now understood that the refusal to cooperate with law enforcement was just as much about the fear of law enforcement – the belief that by cooperating, more bad than good will come your way from the police – as it was the fear of the perpetrators' revenge.]

Beyond the sensory overload and regulatory angst overwhelming your senses, one of the most depressing features of Shock and Awful was the obsequiousness, skittishness, and general suck-uppishness that campers displayed around cops. It's not that I didn't understand it – any cop could write

34

you up for anything at any time…fair unfair, true, false, right, wrong, it didn't matter. And writing you up could mean that you lose privileges (phone, computer, visits), get sent to the SHU to never to return, or lose good time meaning a lengthening of sentence. I saw the youngest, strongest, most Alpha-male Black, Spanish, and White men bowing down to the man and this made me both sad and angry. The shock to one's sense of pride may be the most debilitating feature of Shock and Awful.

As I hope this book is as much a guide to significant sustainable weight loss as it is a memoir of my time in federal fat camp, let me translate how Shock and Awful can set the stage for your weight loss program. At the heart of Shock and Awful is this maxim: Comfort is your enemy.

In the Jailbird Diet, the cushy couch is the enemy; the comfortable chair is the enemy. The warm bed, the unfettered access to a refrigerator and/or pantry is the enemy, the TV remote is the enemy.

Wake up early, get out of bed, get outside as quickly as possible. Nearly every day I spent in prison, I was outside with my chair, books, writing materials, MP3 player and headset from 8:00 A.M. till 7:30 P.M., returning inside for brief periods of eating and bathroom. When you lie down it is to sleep, nothing else. I slept on a 2-inch foam mattress in a 2-foot-wide bed and when my head hit the pillow I was out. Do not work, watch television, write, converse or do anything for that matter, other than sleep, in bed.

In the Jailbird Diet, showers are for cleaning, not a substitute for a spa treatment. The toilet is not a platform for anything other than bodily functions. The kitchen is not a communal living space, it is a fueling station. The refrigerator is not a bookshelf to be browsed – at 4:30 it should be locked until 6:30 the next morning.

Placing comfort as the enemy does not have to mean risking life and limb to sleep in an upper bunk; nor does it mean having to live in perpetual angst as I did in my first few months at camp. It does mean stripping your daily life of moments of ease; denying your body of aaah moments; creating an environment of personal space that forces you to look inward for comfort, joy, and peace of mind. If sitting on a plastic chair or metal cafeteria table is your only option during every waking hour of the day, you will spend far more time walking or running. If television is not an option, you will spend far more time reading, writing, and cross-wording. If food is never fresh nor nutritious, eating will become less about dining and more like refueling.

Shock and awful is metaphor – the stripping your life of everything that makes daily existence pleasurable and replacing it with the sparse, the barren, the rudimentary: the plastic chair rather than the couch; a hard platform bed with a thin mattress and one small sized pillow; an alarm clock that wakes you with an jolt; a quick shower; no more than 15-minutes maximum spent at any meal; no opening the refrigerator except the three times of the day to retrieve food; cooking only immediately before lunch and dinner if necessary and for no more than 60 minutes all in; television for one-hour – 30-minutes of local news; 30-minutes of national news. No internet beyond minimal email communications with family. No tweets. No Instagram. No sex.

Now you are ready. You have created the wasteland which you now must cross to achieve the weight loss goal you have set for yourself. Next step: Preparing your mind and body for the journey.

Chapter 3
Lay of the Land

Fairton Camp can best be envisioned both literally and figuratively as an island
– a place cut off from the free world by a thick woods spreading on the western
edge of the camp along Fairton-Millville Road in Millville New Jersey; a spit
of land running north-south parallel to that road – roughly a 1/4 mile long by
1/10 mile wide; a collection of warehouses, trailers, play areas, and parkland
between the woods to the West and the service road wrapping around the
medium security prison (Fairton FCI) to the East of the camp.

The housing unit, kitchen/cafeteria, bathroom buildings and the
administrative and camper service trailers (chapel/laundry/multi-purpose
room) – are all laid out on the northern end of the island with what I came to
call Central Park and the oval track surrounding it laid out on the southern end.

Having spent over 2,000 hours walking this track, I know every step of it
by heart.

I always walked counterclockwise around the track like Muslims in the
Tawaf – that point of the Muslim pilgrimage in Mecca when the faithful circle
the Kaaba (Black Stone) seven times in a counterclockwise direction. When I
saw campers circling the track in the opposite direction, it felt wrong to me;
like a Muslim circling the Kaaba in the wrong direction. I never engaged in
such sacrilege.

My walks began at the light pole on the outside of the southwest corner of
the track where Joe would place his stones – a stone for each lap completed (I
kept my lap count through a series of finger positions from one lap – right
index finger extended – to right fist closed for five laps). Twenty paces down
on the inside of the track was the workout station for chin ups, pushups, dips
and the aerial perch for those who just wanted to hang out and talk to let's

say…themselves (aerial positioning allowed for contraband cell phone conversations with a bird's eye view of cop movement).

Down the track another 20 paces were the cat food bowls – one on the inside of the track, two on the outside of the track just inside the fence line. By my count, there were four cats; I named them by their colors – Butterscotch, Zorro (white with a black strip across its eyes), Blackie, and Gray. I think Butterscotch died as one night by the windows of the phone room, I heard the plaintive cries of a cat and never saw Butterscotch in the park thereafter.

As I traveled south down the track away, I crossed over the faces; stones protruding from the smoothed dirt track that appeared as noses, eyes, mouths, and chins which I fancied were the ancestors of the Lenape Tribe – the native Americans who roamed these woods 300 years ago.

Moving south beyond the faces to the turn of the track at the southwest corner of the island, a dirt road runs to the to the right or west about 1/4 mile to the gun range. As a prisoner, listening to the sound of gunfire coming from a gun range takes on a whole new meaning; the men and women of law enforcement honing their skills to take aim at prisoners who dare to attempt escape. Of course, this was not a present danger as no cop I ever saw carried a firearm. Then again, it was not so theoretical a danger when someone at the range decided to shoot off a tear gas-like substance that wafted on a northwest wind to the camp causing campers to run inside for cover (this happened twice during my stay).

[Aside: This experience made watching the tear gassing of peaceful protesters in Lafayette Park – with the help of BOP SWAT teams all the more strange; I never thought the practicing at the Fairton gun range would sharpen the skills of BOP personnel firing on a gathering 'in the free world.' How naive!]

At the southern tip of the track, the woods filled in beyond the fence line to meet the service road that ran back the length of the track on its eastern side. In this section of woods stood one large dark brown tree with its thick trunk branching into a candelabra of leafless arms reaching up to the sky as if pleading with the gods for the souls of the men crossing its path; like Shiva the destroyer waiting to carry me from this life to the next – and all the other lives that followed. As Shiva is honored on his holiest days by the smoking of marijuana or hashish, I found it somewhat fitting that campers would choose this end of the island, at the foot of Shiva, to smoke their joints when the sun went down.

Rounding the track down the back stretch (always welcome as it marks the beginning of a slight decline in the track which, by lap 50, you can start to feel), leaving Shiva over my right shoulder, you travel parallel to the service road that leads from the main public road to the parking lot for the medium security prison then runs to the south beyond the camp up to the oh so mysterious Sierra building – a prison run by the FBI housing high-profile rats and those still cooperating in on-going law enforcement activity who could not be housed with the general population in the Medium or any other facility without fear of bodily harm or worse (or so I was told).

As you make the turn for home you pass the labyrinth. While many federal prisons have bocce courts – an aspect of federal camps that leads reporters to use the moniker Club Fed to describe them – I know of none other that has a labyrinth in its marketing brochure.

If you didn't know that the circles of stones within circles of stones was a labyrinth there was a sign at the entrance which simply read, "The Labyrinth." In my first few months, the labyrinth was meticulously groomed on a daily basis by AC of the camper landscape crew.

[Aside: AC was a middle-aged white bald, tatted-up hulk of a man who was a former state kickboxing/martial arts champ and rode with some pretty tough fellows before finding his way to prison. He was the first of the very few campers to approach me opening up to discuss his motorcycle gang past which I found fascinating. When I asked him about the date of the hit placed on one of the gang leaders, he matter-of-factly pulled up his shirt to show the date tattooed across his right rib cage.

AC was also the first to show me true kindness at camp.

As I laid out in Shock and Awful, not knowing where to sit, stand, or walk is one of the greatest sources of anxiety for a new camper; never more so than when the chow hall is converted to TV room and every stackable chair is moved off the walls or carried in from the housing unit for nightly viewing. Positioning is coveted and protected as it determines which TV – Black, Spanish, White, or Sport – you would be closest to and, therefore, have the best viewing sightline. A week into my camp experience and I still had not figured out where I was to put my chair but I had to put it somewhere as my upper bunk assignment made lounging in the housing unit a non-starter. So I am at the double door entry to the chow hall looking for a place for my chair when AC comes up to me and says, "Follow me."

He walks me and my chair to a space toward the far-left corner of the chow hall between an older white camper, Coach, and a young white camper, Harry. He tells me to put my chair in between the two. Coach objects telling AC that the spot my chair is now sitting in another camper's who had moved his chair temporarily to play poker. AC told Coach that this spot was his, that he gave it to the poker playing camper when the poker player came to the camp, and that when the poker player was released from camp next week, AC was bequeathing this spot to me. Coach quickly backed down and I had a seat in the television room from that moment till the day ten months later I packed out for the Medium; a perfect position – closest to the Sports TV – for my viewing priority was almost exclusively sports.

To this day, I cannot explain why AC bestowed this act of kindness upon me. I was a nobody of little value who kept to himself. As you will read later on in Chapter X Pandemic, there were inexplicable acts of humanity that took place in the camp on a daily basis; acts of kindness and generosity at times carried out by the roughest and toughest of campers. AC showing me to my place in TV land was one such act. But I digress – onto the labyrinth!]

I never asked why AC was so devoted to grooming the labyrinth. Few campers chose to enter it: Pancho, the camp Papist, would walk around it rubbing his rosary beads; Jeff the camp New-Ager would do yoga there, Suicide Mark (a moniker bestowed on him for his perpetual gloom) would catch a tan on the bench at the labyrinth's center. And as I passed the labyrinth day after day, it was hard not to see the symbolism of the labyrinth in the woods – a place where prisoners can become transformed like the characters in Shakespeare's "A Mid-Summer Nights Dream" to be saved by Puck or like the Athenian youth who enter it to either be killed by the Minotaur or saved by Theseus. The woods and all within it had the power to transform. I am the proof of it.

Whether you have a track, a path in the woods, tree-lined streets or a parking lot, designating a place or places for your daily walk is one of the first orders of business in the Jailbird Diet.

I was very fortunate that the federal camp to which I was sent had a track built into a wooded area making it feel more like a community park than a federal penitentiary. If you can, do what Thoreau did: walk in the woods every day and take some time each day to revel in the magnificence of God's creation all around it.

Chapter 4
Solitude and SCUBA

"Our life is frittered away by detail. An honest man has hardly need to count more than his ten fingers, or in extreme cases, he may add his ten toes, and lump the rest. Simplify, simplify, simplify. I say let your affairs be two or three, and not a hundred or a thousand. Instead of a million, count a half dozen, and keep your accounts on your thumb-nail. In the midst of this chopping sea of civilized life, such are the clouds and storms, and quicksands and thousand-and-one items to be allowed for, that a man has to live, if he would not founder and go to the bottom and not make his port at all, by dead reckoning, and he must be a great calculator indeed who succeeds. Simplify. Simplify."
Walden p. 51

A federal prison is a perfect environment in which to begin the process of radical life simplification.

I arrived at Fairton FCI at the scheduled hour of 2:00 P.M. It took two hours from the time I said goodbye to my wife, Shelly, and oldest daughter, Lucy, to be processed, stripped, outfitted with clothing and bedding and placed at my bed for the 4:00 P.M. mandatory stand-up count – a time when all prisoners are expected to stand quietly at the foot of their beds to be counted present by the housing unit and kitchen cops. After the count, I asked the housing unit cop if there was anywhere I needed to be or anything I needed to do. He looked at me as if I was speaking in tongues.

A week later, I walked into the office of the Camp Counselor.

[Aside: Titles are a politically correcting vehicle for the BOP: a "camp counselor" does not counsel, he sets the rules and enforces them; a "case manager" does not manage your case, he pushes papers to other offices to manage it; your "team unit meeting" is never done in a team – a one-on-one affair typically lasting less than a couple minutes of signing papers.

Sitting in the counselor's office, waiting for him to end a call, I looked around the office; on each wall, motivational quotes or words which, in and of themselves, were meant to convey some meaning to prisoners. This seems to be a BOP technique for prison decoration. In the 7' × 9' cell in which I am now writing this, I can look out the slit window on my prison door to the common area of Delta Wing Left in the medium security facility. It is decorated with prisoner-painted art: a ghoulish Nicholas-Cage-Ghost-Rider skull with a cigarette/joint in mouth with the words, "Don't let your addiction get a hold on you"; the columns ringing the common area are covered with the words "Caring," "Responsibility," "Role Model" running down them. In the camp counselor's office, they were primarily the quotes of John Wayne, which led one of my favorite inmates, let's call him Little Big Man, to reflect one day: "All I know John Wayne was famous for was killing Niggers and Indians."]

My reason for visiting the camp counselor was to begin to work on a plan I had devised to do something meaningful with my time in federal prison: use the inmates to form a dial-test and focus group of the Democrat presidential debates. The idea was fairly straight-forward: have the inmates watch the presidential debate, and while doing so, score the candidate performance in real-time at 5-minute intervals on sheets of paper I provided them. The inmate population, skewing primarily younger African American/Latino with little education and no voting history, presented a universe of the electorate rarely if ever polled. This new set of data should, it seemed to me, be of value in the free world.

I also thought, selfishly, it would free up one of the four televisions in the chow hall for debate watching and away from the normal viewing choices: Black TV (Black Ink Chicago/Basketball Wives/Cruise Girl/Love and Hip Hop Atlanta); Spanish TV (Exatlon Games – think hard bodies on the beach playing state fair games – knock down the pins/throw the hoop on the animals – then jump, slide, and climb through water, sand or mud); White TV (some action movie on FX or the SYFY Channel); and Sports TV (baseball or NBA Summer League).

If my program was certified by the "Education Director," (another misnomer as we shall see) inmates would watch the debate, get credit for doing so, which would, theoretically, translate into time off their sentence – a benefit clearly worth giving up their reality TV options for.

Upon laying out my idea, the camp counselor looked at me and said, "Mr. Smukler, you will find that the biggest problem inmates have when they come to Fairton is time management."

I quickly understood why.

In the first six weeks at Fairton FCI, I was required on a daily basis to be anywhere and do anything only twice each day for 15–30 minutes; be at my bed for the 4:00 P.M. and 10:00 P.M. counts Monday and Friday with one additional count at 10:30 A.M. on Saturday and Sunday. Every other minute of every other hour of every day was mine to do with as I pleased: sleep all day – no problem – some pretty much did; weight room, bocce, handball, hoops; read, write, watch TV. Any, all, none. Until you were assigned a job, the time was yours, almost all of the time.

The last time I recall time ever being mine to do with as I pleased, owing no explanation for the how I chose to spend it was college or law school post-exams or maybe at summer camp when the evening was called "Hot Stove" (I don't know why) and you could do what you like before returning to your bunk.

What so much time created for me was the opportunity to fill it with a schedule that was as regimented as any I created for myself in the free world.

Breakfast always between 6:00 and 6:30 – not because I wanted to but because I had to. You get to the chow hall after 6:30 A.M. and the ½ pints of milk delivered in two crates might be gone (not that there wasn't enough to go around; there was plenty to go around if every camper took just one ½ pint for themselves; but campers always took two and some took six or eight; some campers were paid in Fairton currency – a three oz. tinfoil package of mackerel = $1.00 – to deliver milk for those who did not want to wake pre-6:30 to get it themselves).

After breakfast, make your bed.

[Aside: making your bed was a requirement and, I am told, was taken seriously in higher security prisons where bunk inspections were routine and the slowest and sloppiest were penalized by being called to the chow hall last. This incentivized bed making led to a different sleeping experience for those who had dropped down versus those, like myself, who had self-surrendered. Those who dropped down almost never slept under sheets and covers choosing

44

rather to sleep on top of a made bed with just a blanket over them. That way, in the morning or whenever they chose to rise, they would simply fold the blanket and put it at the foot of the bed and, voila! bed made – no fuss no muss. I on the other hand had two sheet and two blankets to crawl under each night and straighten out every morning.]

After the bed made, a quick shower. As ¾ of the camp was now out of the housing unit and up the road at their jobs (food warehouse – maintenance – landscaping – garage – for-profit Comcast modem stripping operation called Unicorp) the showers were left wide open. Not having to worry about traffic in the showers was one of the first ways I simplified my day-to-day life at camp.

Then out to the wooded area, what I called Central Park, with my books, crossword puzzles, writing materials, MP3 player, headset and chair to begin a schedule that rotated these disciplines around a walking schedule that had me walking the track that circumnavigated the park each hour. In for lunch at 10:15 for 15 minutes then back out to the park; back in for count at 4:00 P.M. followed by dinner. Then back out to the park at 5:00 P.M. to repeat the process till darkness fell with a break sometimes for local news at 6:00 P.M. and national news at 6:30 P.M. 8:30 was outdoor recall, then into the chow hall converted to TV Room till 10 P.M. for count; bed at 11:00. Next Day: repeat same. Next Day: repeat same.

As you will see in the chapters to come, it was the regimentation of my existence at camp that made all the difference; it provided me the structure in which to engage a weight loss program that significantly dropped the amount of food I ate and drank, burned a lot more calories than I consumed, devoting hours of the day to walking around the camp track, mental gymnastics in-between, and living hunger free while doing so.

I recognize the freedom to define one's schedule like this is not typically afforded those in the free world; it is called the Jailbird Diet for a reason. Your ability to build into a work and family schedule a devotion to hours that will press your body not just physically, but mentally and emotionally will be perhaps the toughest part of this journey. As you will see, this is not just a time commitment, it is a commitment to solitude; a commitment to freeing yourself not just from junk food but junk life – junk relationships, junk conversations, junk gossip, junk news, and junk entertainment.

But if you succeed at this regimentation, you will take hunger out of the dieting equation and allow your body to consume fewer calories on a daily basis than it burns over a sustained period of time.

Oh. And whatever happened to my proposal to create an education program centered around the watching of presidential debates? It was never acted upon.

In a land-locked, swimming pool-less, spit of ground, 40 miles from the nearest body of water, the "Education Director" introduced a new prison-approved class for the campers instead:

Scuba Diving.

Welcome to Camp Fairton.

Chapter 5
Cleanse: Toxic Television

If you are strictly adhering to the Jailbird Diet, you will be walking or running between three and six hours a day. What you do in between your walks and after you come inside for the day is equally important to sustaining short-term weight loss. In all of your non-walking, non-sleeping hours, the Jailbird Diet requires you to first cleanse.

While many newer diets encourage a cleanse to rid your body of toxins, that is not the cleanse I am talking about. I am speaking of cleansing the toxic parts of your 'non-food diet' from your day-to-day activities as much and as soon as you can. Once you have achieved this cleansing, you will begin to feed your brain with new super foods that will take away the hunger that so often kills short-term weight loss.

Just as you will pay attention (and record) everything that you put in your mouth during your weight loss journey, so too will you pay attention to all the other things that you allow your body to consume during this time. You need not record this consumption but you do need to pay scrupulous attention to it.

To this end, I now provide a nineteenth century transcendentalist's guide to non-food junk food or what I call the Toxic Trilogy: Toxic Television, Toxic Social Media, and Toxic Relationships.

The biggest purveyor of junk in your non-food diet is television.

According to a Nielsen report, United States adults are watching five hours and four minutes of television per day on average (35.5 h/week, slightly more than 77 days per year). Older people watch more (less than 50 h/week), younger people less (more than 20 h/week), both with a seasonal pattern that peaks in the winter months.

If removing television altogether were a realistic possibility in the modern world, I would say do it and end the chapter here. Thoreau went cold turkey from his version of television – the town print office – by simply walking in the woods.

"There was such a rush, as I hear, the other day at one of the offices to learn the foreign news by the latest arrival...news which I seriously think a ready wit may write a twelve month, or twelve years beforehand with sufficient accuracy. As for Spain, for instance, if you know how to throw in Don Carlos and the Infanta, and Don Pedro and Seville and Grenada, from time to time in the right proportions – and serve up a bull-fight when other entertainments fail, it will be true to the letter, and give us as good an idea of the exact state of ruin in Spain as the most succinct and lucid reports under this head in the newspapers. If one may judge who rarely looks into the newspapers, nothing new does ever happen in foreign parts, a French Revolution not excepted."
Walden p. 53

Using Thoreau's approach, we can go beyond the most simple and effective approach to junk television removal – going cold turkey – by differentiating our television viewing in a way that creates ground rules for watching; a system that I employed in prison which limited my television viewing to only that which I called "news" avoiding almost everything else which I characterized as "gossip."

"I am sure that I never read any memorable news in a newspaper. If we read of one man robbed, or murdered, or killed by accident, or one cow run over on the Western railroad, or one mad dog killed, or one lot of grasshoppers in the winter – we need never read of another. One is enough. If you are acquainted with the principle, what do you care for a myriad of instances and applications? To a philosopher, all news, as it is called is gossip, and they who edit it and read it are old women over tea."
Walden, p. 53

With limited exceptions which I will discuss further on, television is nothing but gossip, gossip about gossip, or scripted gossip. And gossip is the junkiest of junk food. Think of television, particularly day time television – talk shows, soap operas, and cable news – as one big candy and chips vending

48

machine. Whatever happens to your brain when you are eating junk food, I am pretty sure that's happening when you watch daytime television.

Drastically reducing your television time on the Jailbird Diet should not be as difficult as you think. If you have constructed the right shock and awful framework, you will not devote nearly as much time to a passive activity such as television watching; if that doesn't do it, walking three to six hours a day should.

While studies have shown a link between weight gain and binge-watching television – a link primarily driven by the sedentary nature of short-term television viewing – none that I know of makes the connection between *different types of television programming* and weight gain. None caution, as the Jailbird Diet does, that watching, for example, reality television undermines short-term attempts at weight loss while watching real news, sports, weather, and business news, actually promotes a healthy weight loss regime. All I can tell you is that I do not think I could have sustained a 10-month weight loss program losing 100 pounds without making a distinction between healthy television and junk food television.

Such a distinction may, at first blush, seem quite easy. Take away reality television (all game shows and competitions), soap operas, entertainment "newscasts," and situation comedies on broadcast networks, and you have cut out a large swath of American television viewing. Applying Thoreau's lexicon, it's all just gossip, gossip about gossip, or scripted gossip.

But what about television news and, in particular cable news? Surely this television format must be considered part of a healthy viewing diet. Not so fast. I find television news, be it cable, broadcast, daytime or primetime, to provide some of the most toxic forms of television broadcast today. And I should know.

When I walked into camp, I was in the top 1% of the 1% of daytime news consumers. I watched cable news networks from the moment I rose in the morning till the national news at 6:30 in the evening. I would begin my day with Morning Joe on MSNBC, flip to CNN in the 9:00 A.M. bloc then hit FOX from 11:00 A.M. till 1:00 P.M., back to MSNBC till 4:00 P.M. with CNN's Jake Tapper, flip to FOX' Neal Cavuto at 5:00 P.M. then local news at 6:00 and national news at 6:30. It took a nineteenth century Transcendentalist and a twenty-first century politician to show me the error of my ways.

One of the greatest services Donald Trump and Fox News have done for America is to show us all that what constitutes news is as subjective as what constitutes art. Those who believe there is a distinction between news and fake news would be much more accurate if they distinguished between news and gossip; they would find that what constitutes news is, as Thoreau laid it out, a very small slice of the reality pie we are served up each day; the rest nothing more than gossip. Consuming news is a healthy part of your daily diet; consuming gossip is no better than hitting the vend-a-teria. It is the difference between eating a bag of carrots and a bag of Double Stuffed Oreos. Treat news not as fake news or real news but as news versus gossip and you will quickly begin to remove a great deal of toxic material from your diet.

The Supreme Court, and the news coverage of it, is the perfect example of pure political news devoid of gossip. This provides the model for determining gossip from news across all current event programming. The Court does not speak about matters before it issues its rulings. The Supreme Court only makes news when it acts. NBC News's Pete Williams covering the Supreme Court is carrots. Now apply this rule to other aspects of news coverage and you will begin to reposition your television news viewing habits.

First, let's look at national news on the legacy media networks: the perfect example of pure gossip masquerading as news.

One night I was watching the ABC Evening News with David Muir (I did not get to select which newscasts we watched inside though I don't believe the rules that apply to Muir are that much different when applied to Lester Holt or Nora O'Donnel); he reads the story of an explosion at a paper mill in Maine. No one was killed, no one was injured. Just a big explosion caught on video. This is no more newsworthy than watching a three-year old ride his tricycle into a wall on one of the inmates' favorite shows, "Ridiculousness." Paper mill explosion in Maine no one hurt, no one injured = Double Stuffed Oreos.

The House or Senate passes legislation or votes down legislation – News. Politicians talking about passing or voting down legislation – Gossip. World leaders threatening or promising anything – Gossip. World leaders launching an attack or signing a peace agreement – News. The president signs/vetoes legislation or issues and executive order – News. Live presidential news conferences – mostly gossip. Live press secretary news conferences (particularly in the Trump-era) – always gossip.

For the vast majority of national television news, I am simply pointing out these distinctions for academic purposes. There is a self-regulating mechanism that allows you to separate out the toxic intake when consuming television news – one that separates the carrots from the Oreos without the need of a clicker constantly at the ready to mute out the gossip. Technology has provided the answer and, once again, we have Fox News, more particularly Roger Ailes, who, if we are to believe the TV drama, The Loudest Voice, developed the news crawl on 911 to heighten coverage of the attacks.

News is delivered by almost every cable news outlet in the news crawl that runs as a constant feed across the bottom of the television screen. If you want to know the real news that is being generated in newsrooms across the political spectrum, jump from MSNBC to CNN to FOX with the sound muted and just read the crawl. That is where you will find the news. This is precisely how I consumed television news on a daily basis for ten months in prison.

During the daytime hours, when I happened to be in the chow hall, I would watch the White TV whether it was Fox News or CNN (it was never MSNBC) without my headphones on – only reading the crawl moving across the bottom of the screen. I found this to be perfectly sufficient to keep me up to speed on current events at any given hour of the day. If you couple this with reading just the headlines and first few graphs of the A section of the New York Times and Wall Street Journal (as I did, fortunate enough to have these delivered to the housing unit on a daily basis), you will be more than abreast of the news. Your time with this cable news junk food will diminish drastically as it did for me and you will still be a well-informed American prepared to do your part for Democracy whether in the polling booth or, more often, around the water cooler (if we ever get back to working out of offices) or at a cocktail party.

But what about the pandemic? Surely a pandemic is news. To which I respond, it was news when it hit; it will be news when a vaccine arrives on the scene to inoculate us from it; and it will be news when a cure is found to prevent our succumbing to it. Watch it in the news crawl. Cable news makes pandemic viewing easier as it places on screen the global and US death counts during almost every story. Everything else is deep fried jalapeño poppers.

How about the police shooting of an unarmed Black man? Or the riots spawned by such shootings?

"If you are acquainted with the principle, what do you care for a myriad of instances and applications?"

Surely in America we are acquainted with the principle. I don't find it any more disrespectful of the Black Lives Matter movement to make a conscious decision to not watch peaceful BLM marches or their non-peaceful offshoots than to not watch racist marches in Charlottesville and their non-peaceful offshoots. The hundredth video of a march for racial justice or race-baiting conduct is no more newsworthy than the first video you saw of such a protest and, in my life time, I have seen hundreds.

Exception: when the news crawl alerts me to the president's decision to use tear gas on peaceful protesters in Lafayette Park, I find the video and turn the audio up or better yet in the free world seek out the best video to see what happened. Because that is something I have never seen before. Once I have seen it, however, I do not devote one second of my time to the talking heads discussing it. *"Acquainted with the principle, don't care about the myriad of instances and applications."*

While national news can be parsed like this and consumed via non-audio news crawls, local news is a different animal where there generally is no crawl. According to Pew Research Center, local news viewing has been steadily declining since 2007 when over 25 million Americans watched both early evening and late night news to over 20 million in 2017 (https://www.pewresearch.org/wp-content/uploads/sites/8/2018/07/State-of-the-News-Media_2017-Archive.pdf#page=30).

In prison, I came to recognize that almost all local news is gossip. How many fires in North Philadelphia does one need to see before one recognizes that he no longer needs that as part of his news diet? I have seen thousands of them. The drug deal murder with the innocent victim caught in the crossfire is no different than the next Kardashian anything. The words of a local politician cutting taxes or raising taxes, are no less gossip than the words of Mario Lopez telling us of the breakup of the next Hollywood "It" couple.

Now that we have dispensed with a good part of the 77 days of television viewing Americans spend in front of the television, what is left of television that can be considered nutritious? What television viewing can remain part of the Jailbird Diet? Here's the list.

Live sporting event, sport scores and recaps.

The weather.

Business news only as it relates to actual transactions and market moves.

Arts and Entertainment, only the reviews, not the who's sleeping with who stuff.

Sports

The summer at a prison is the low point of sports viewing (in a non-Olympic year). Baseball took a distant second on the Sports TV to Summer NBA and the most popular summer sports shows, the NBA Summer League and the free agency sweepstakes.

But when the calendar moves toward the end of the summer, the Sports TV goes on steroids as football season approaches. The television viewing was intimately tied to the robust wagering industry spawned by the underground economy. I set up a mackerel account with the bookies (mackerel packs as we shall discuss later being the currency of choice at Fairton) and watched games Wednesday through Mondays. On Saturday and Sunday mornings, I spent some brief time watching the betting shows to better inform my wagering. Betting became the way that I engaged in sports viewing that I would not normally watch.

But my sports viewing rule was clear: I watched games in real time. I did not watch any of the sports television that comprised talking heads opining about games played or games to come. Live games are news. Wagering television is news. Sports news – who won and lost, who was traded or injured – is news. Whether Dak Prescott should receive the Dallas Cowboys' franchise designation from Jerry Jones is gossip – as all other sports television is gossip.

Weather. Weather is always news. I suspect if you watch the Weather Channel, it can become gossip but the Weather Channel is not an option at a federal prison. Weather, however, becomes gossip when it is used by national news operations to scare. No news outlet does this better than ABC News which, almost nightly, seemed shocked to find storms that stretch from Texas to Wisconsin moving east across the country. As long as I have been watching weather in North America – over five decades – it is not news to see a storm front moving west to east across the US; and not that unusual for these fronts to stretch from northern states to the Deep South.

Hurricanes and the run-up to hitting land are news. Watching a reporter bracing against the elements, video of telephone polls down, people being saved from flooding – gossip.

Business News. The markets moving up and down, companies being merged, acquired, sold, or bankrupted is news. For those working in the financial sector or day trading, I suspect that financial rumors, CEO projections, and talking-head analysis is news as it informs buying and selling decisions; for me it was just gossip.

Arts, Entertainment

Movie trailers and theater and book reviews are news; all else is gossip.

Of course, beyond live sporting events, I was not tempted with television viewing options in nightly prime time that drew me away from the library I had amassed at my bunk. So let me address night time television viewing as the options in the free world for such entertainment went far beyond the choices I was presented each night on the Black, White, and Spanish televisions. How one distinguishes junk from non-junk in the hours between dinner and bedtime is just as important (if not more so as your ability, particularly in the winter months, to be moving outside becomes more limited) as the decisions you make during the day.

Prime time viewing requires no less demarcation between gossip and non-gossip. It does not have a technology solution like a news crawl that can differentiate the healthy from the junk for you. As a rule, taking out all primetime television would be a great start to your Jailbird Diet. But I totally understand that such a solution may be too Draconian even for a Jailbirder. My suggestion for night time viewing is to find shows that challenge your mind to think through the plot lines and dialogue; avoid all reality television and situation comedies; focus on episodic series or movies in which the plot lines are carried more by dialogue than by action sequences.

Stay away from everything that prisoners gravitated toward during TV time: No movies on the SiFi Channel or FX which glorify CGI at the expense of meaningful dialogue; no reality shows like Girls Cruise, Black Inc Chicago, Love&HipHop Atlanta, or Basketball Wives; No Exatlon Games (Exatlon is a self-described "sports-reality format where two teams of physically fit and sportive contestants...chosen after certain sports and condition tests, compete in highly challenging parkours, or obstacle course, to perform at their highest level").

If you can distinguish between junk foods and nutritious foods without looking at a nutrition label, you can distinguish between junk and nutritious viewing equally as intuitively. It is the same way Justice Potter Stewart decided the seminal 1973 case on free speech and pornography, Miller v. California, defining pornography as no more than, "I know it when I see it."

If you follow this guide to television viewing, you should cut your day time viewing to a bare minimum, reserve one hour at most for local and national news, then allow yourself some television time between dinner and bedtime but scrupulously evaluate your choices to place programming that challenges your brain with dialogue (movies/streaming series) or live action sequences (sports).

Science

My favorite stories in newspapers and television news are those that deal with science. Discoveries, whether they be in the field of life sciences, astrophysics, archeology, whatever, is always news and very healthy to consume. You can never go wrong on your diet watching the PBS series, Nova. Pretty sure most programing on Nat Geo is going to be good for you.

Self Help Television

Some of the most popular daytime television programming at camp were the Do-It-Yourself shows primarily focused on home building and renovation. These I distinguish from the medical self-help shows, most popular of which was Dr. Pimple Popper (yes this is a real show) which is as un-nutritious as it sounds.

The Jailbird Television Guide:

(1) never watch television during the day (with the exception of live sporting events); (2) watch news only via the news crawl; (3) non-news viewing should be restricted by hours (non-walking/activity between dinner and bedtime) and content (dialogue driven scripted episodic series or movies); and (4) always watch with a crossword or some other puzzle in hand. Television, regardless of the time or type of show and with rare exceptions, should not be consumed in a vacuum. Whatever is happening in the brain that ameliorates hunger pangs, is not triggered by television watching in the absence of other brain activity which, for me, meant cross-wording. See the section, Cross-Wording.

As I have said, the science around television viewing and weight loss does not make the connection between the types of television viewed and success or failure in weight loss. It does, however, make a very convincing case for the drastic reduction in television viewing.

Chapter 6
Cleanse: Snarknado

Henry David Thoreau did not have to flee the television or the Internet when he left Concord for his walk in the woods. But applying his view of news and gossip to television, which would not be invented for another 82 years (1927), can be equally applied to social media platforms which would not come into existence for another 159 years (The Facebook, 2004).

The United States has one of the highest social network penetration rates in the world. In 2019, over 246 million Americans were using social networks to post pictures, like and comment on content by others, or send private messages. With over 70 percent of the U.S. population holding a social media account, these platforms and services have become some of the most popular online activities of the past decades. By 2023, the number of social network users in the United States is forecast to increase to approximately 257 million.

Social media is primarily used for entertainment, communication, news coverage, and business purposes. Among the various types of platforms, online users in the U.S. most frequently visit social networks, photo-sharing platforms, microblogging, and instant messaging services. These websites and apps have become an integral part of many American internet users' daily routines. While the average daily usage time ranged from 30 minutes to two hours according to a 2019 survey, this figure will likely increase as a result of the coronavirus (COVID-19) pandemic. As many Americans started to self-isolate at home in March 2020, social media and other types of digital communication saw an unprecedented spike in usage nationwide.

Facebook is the most popular social network in the United States based on monthly active users. As of April 2020, the platform recorded over 190 million account holders in the United States and maintained a market share of over 43 percent. Mobile is an integral part of Facebook's leading position in the market, as the networking giant is also the most popular mobile social networking app in the United States by reach, engagement, and audience. Seeing that accounted for 83 percent of social media visits in the U.S. by the end of 2019, the importance of mobile-friendly user interfaces cannot be overstated.

https://www.statista.com/topics/3196/social-media-usage-in-the-united-states/

If the largest bloc of time to be simplified in your day is your television watching, the next largest bloc is, most likely, social media: a form of junk food potentially far more toxic to your system and debilitating to your diet than television.

There is no Internet in prison. My prison online experience consisted of six terminals (four or five of which were operable at any given time) ringing the room called the library just off the western wall of the chow hall. These terminals were not for accessing the Internet; they were for email communications through the BOP's closed intranet. Email could only be sent and received to/from BOP approved contacts and limited by time and words: 30 minutes per use with 30-minute lockout before the next 30-minute use. Email minutes cost money which was deducted directly from your BOP account.

While it is easy to describe much of what I was going through during my camp experience, it is hard to describe just how liberating the removal of email from my life was for me; If, God forbid, you find your way to a BOP facility (or, perhaps you live like the UniBomber in the middle of the Montana wilderness) you will very quickly understand what I mean. The liberation one feels when access to the Internet is taken from you is real and almost instantaneous.

I fully recognize that removing oneself from daily contact with social media platforms is not going to be easy, but if it were easy 75% of the word diet wouldn't be die.

With rare exceptions, all of social media is gossip.

I will first give you the exception in the hopes that you see how rare it is.

I signed up for a Twitter account in the second week of April 2013. I did so in an effort to better experience my oldest daughter Lucy's running in the Boston Marathon one week later, on April 13th. The day of the marathon I was in my car when the news hit: there was a bombing at the finish line of the marathon. I called Lucy and she picked up; she told me that I need not worry, things had gotten screwed up with her running group and she was not running in the marathon after all. Subsequently she told me that this was all a lie, she was actually on the course running when she took my call but didn't want me to worry. File this under just another clueless dad episode of which there were far more than I choose to remember or would ever commemorate in writing.

Using Twitter to track your daughter's marathon experience is one of the best and, in my mind, healthiest uses of a social media platform. But that is not how I used Twitter on Marathon Day. Later that evening, I was having dinner out with my middle daughter Phoebe. Twitter was tracking the Boston Police Department and FBI manhunt for the brother suspects on the streets of Boston and the surrounding neighborhoods. As Lucy was in school at Boston College, this tracking was for me far more than just prurient interest. It was news. It was riveting. And it was the first and last time that I tracked a news event through a web app.

I have used Twitter, Snapchat, Instagram to track Phoebe's performances on stage and our youngest, Camille's, performance on the tennis court. In post-incarceration pandemic, Shelly and I use Zoom to see and communicate with family and friends. But if you are serious about following the Jailbird Diet, you must be serious about limiting your access to social media platforms and, more broadly, your time on the Internet.

Twitter, in its character limitation, is almost by definition, gossip. Facebook is gossip. Snapchat, and Instagram pictures of family and friends, not gossip; pictures of what they are eating for dinner or that cute little cocktail, purely gossip. Stay away from TikTok (unless its kids, grandkids or friends performing) and YouTube as much as possible. If that means carving out a 15-minute bloc of personal time each day to engage with the Internet, set your clock accordingly, and get in and out of it.

Social media rule to live by in the free world on the Jailbird Diet: Never place your computer or smart phone by your bed.

Chapter 7
Cleanse: The Company You Keep and the Company You Deep (Six)

The concept of Baby Mamas never really came up in conversations, personal or professional, before I went to camp. In prison, it is a concept that is difficult to get away from. Coop had 15 kids by 9 baby mamas. TBone: nine kids, three baby mamas. Weed: five kids, two baby mamas – and he was in his early 30s – just getting started (or so I am told).

I never got into heart-to-heart Baby Mama discussions as to the toll that this number of baby mamas takes on the heart and mind of my fellow campers with the exception of one of my very first conversations with anyone inside. It was my first night and I was welcomed to sit at CrapGame's (not his prison name but one I give him now for his wheeler dealer persona reminiscent of the Don Rickle's role in Kelly's Heroes) bunk to go over my first commissary orders. Across from CrapGame was L., head chef for the Spanish car, sitting in his bunk. CrapGame told me of his young son, I told CrapGame of my three daughters, then L. chimed in that he had four kids: a son – thirteen, two daughters – eight, and a son – four. I responded with what I thought would be the normal, "Oh twins. What is that like?" He looked at me like I was crazy. Having two daughters born in the same year was not the sign of twins but the sign of two baby mamas giving birth in the same year. Silly moi.

Baby Mamas, I am sure, are just the tip of the iceberg when it came to toxic relationships for the men of Fairton – and not all, as I subsequently found out, are toxic (some of the most faithful companions of prisoners I knew and saw during visits were their baby mamas). They are, however, an example of toxic relationships that abound inside.

I had my share of toxic relationships from the free world coming in. Some centered around my indictment and conviction – lawyers and associates who lied on the stand at my trial. Some around my work trying to expose an email scandal in Pennsylvania that came to be known as Porngate (a book for another time) – so-called "journalists" who ditched their professional ethics in a daily battle for "click-bait." Some professional relationships who abandoned me the minute the FBI came knocking at their door.

Of course, the mere physical separation that incarceration affords its campers, allows prisoners to shed toxic relationships like a snake sheds its skin. But one need not be physically removed from society to avoid toxic relationships; one does need, however, to be more selective as to the relationships one welcomes in. I will not expound upon this beyond saying that walking in the woods, be it physically as a prisoner or figuratively as one on the Jailbird Diet in the free world, by the very definition, means reducing the number of personal relationships you maintain on a daily basis. By simply reducing the opportunities for social interaction, you will be reducing the influence of toxic relationships on your weight loss program – an influence as damaging as Married at First Sight, a pop star's twitter feed, or the FOX and Friends or Morning Joe App downloaded on your smart phone.

Removing relationships requires establishing decision-making rules around your social life. The rules for me in prison were simple. I did not pro-actively engage in any conversations that dealt with a prisoner's back stories or prior incarcerations; those I did engage in, were conversations that came to me and, for the most part, were short and entirely gossip driven, fueled by the craziness of life in close quarters with 119 men, revolving around the day-to-day existence; they were not conversations about life, love, success, failure, friendships, finances, and God forbid, politics. These relationships based on gossip were as superfluous and as quickly discarded as the tinfoil wrapping on a Chipotle burrito.

I was approached at times to discuss politics which I did in as analytical a fashion as I could muster trying as best I could to avoid picking sides on the partisan divide; everyone wants to pick sides all the time. I avoided it like the plague.

It wasn't that the back stories and prior incarcerations of these men were not interesting. Of those I overheard in the unit or during the rare times one-on-one, most were as fascinating as they were tragic: stories of real pain and heartbreak, of deception, betrayal, and lost love; stories of fortunes made and fortunes lost, stories of an America most citizens don't know and don't want to know. These stories can be as riveting as anything on a crime drama podcast. But as riveting as they may be, I found them to be equally as toxic. Removing them from my daily experience became, therefore, a necessary prerequisite for long-term weight loss. I know this will sound like I am proving a negative. I cannot prove that the absence of toxic relationships was one of the keys to my dieting success. But like toxic TV and toxic social media, the absence of toxic relationships does help foster the environment necessary for significant short-term weight loss.

Chapter 8
Super "Foods:" I'll Take the Tchaikovsky

You are constantly moving. You have simplified your day-to-day timetable. You have now cleared the decks of the toxins that undermine traditional dieting. It is now time to fill your day. It is time for the Super "Foods."

While removing toxic relationships may seem to make your weight loss journey a course too desolate and lonely to undertake, I can tell you it will be anything but lonely if you choose to fill your days with the Super "Foods" of short-term weight loss. These superfoods will fill your time with some of the greatest relationships ever known to man and challenge your mind in ways it has not been challenged before.

The critical component of the Jailbird Diet is the constant challenging of your mind and body throughout the day. Challenging both so much that eating becomes almost a non-event limited in both time and social experience. Food becomes fuel to be consumed like a NASCAR driver pulling into a pit stop.

As you drastically reduce your consumption of television, social media, and toxic relationships – the junk food that historically has consumed large chunks of your waking experience – you must begin to substitute in for this junk, three superfoods to engage your mind and body in whole new ways: music, literature, and puzzles.

As you will see in Part III, Chasing 100, walking comprised the largest single activity of my days at camp, ranging from two to six hours a day depending upon the number of laps around the camp's dirt track I logged. This makes for a lot of music listening.

While Thoreau does reflect on the power of music in some of his other works, he does not take up the subject while in the woods at Walden Pond. Of course, he did not have an MP3 player and an app like Spotify to download his favorite music. He did, however, devote an entire chapter to Sounds.

As I sit at my desk, hawks are circling about my clearing; the tantivy of wild pigeons, flying by twos and threes athwart my view; one perching restless on the white pine boughs behind my house, gives a voice to the air; a fish hawk dimples the glassy surface of the pond and brings up a fish; a mink steals out of the marsh before my door and seizes a frog by the shore; the sedge is bending under the weight of the reed-birds flitting hither and thither, and for the last half-hour I have heard the rattle of railroad cars, now dying away and the reviving like the beat of a partridge.

Walden, p. 64

For Thoreau, it was the sounds of the birds chirping or the train whistle blowing that filled his days. For me, it was the strings of the violin and cello, the blaring of horns, and the scales of the piano that filled my waking and walking hours; classical music my first superfood.

My dad loved listening to classical music. On Sundays, he would listen to the New York Metropolitan opera. On weekdays evenings in the summer, he would sit in Rittenhouse Square, read poetry and listen to WRTI, the classical music station broadcast from Temple University. I never listened to classical music growing up.

My musical tastes ran more to 1970s guitar rock/blues and Reggae. During my professional life, music was only a part of my day when I was in the car coming from a radio station rather than from a Spotify playlist or Pandora. In prison, music was a much bigger part of my life as not one minute of my time walking the track was spent without my MP3 player and headphones on.

Every camper had either a radio or an MP3 player. Not so much for music listening as for television viewing – the audio of the four televisions being set to radio frequencies allowing campers to view any of the televisions at a given time without interfering with another camper's viewing choices. Those who chose to purchase an MP3 player over a radio were doing so primarily to have the added benefit of downloading music. Listening to a playlist, for some campers, was necessary for sleeping in the communal setting of the housing unit; it was not an unusual site to see a camper lying on his bed, headphones on with a knit hat pulled down over his eyes. I chose the MP3 not for downloading purposes but for recharging purposes – the MP3 did not require batteries as it was rechargeable off the camp computers or charging station in the library.

Fairton, in the heart of South Jersey, pulled in radio signals from the Jersey Shore and the Philadelphia media market. I had a wide range of music options to choose from. Initially, I landed on the Oldies station coming out of Vineland – WVLT. I listened so often, I set my walk schedule to the DJs I liked best – Johnny Midnight at 2:00 P.M. and Jerry Blavat (the Geator with the Heater; the Boss with the Hot Sauce) at 5:00 P.M. On Saturday night, Bob Pantana's Dance Party on WOGL came out of Philly. That lasted up until the end of the summer when my listening changed to the classical music station my dad listened to when I was growing up, WRTI. From early morning till 5:00 P.M. (when one of my favorite WRTI segments – Films at Five: Classical Music in the Cinema), I would listen almost exclusively to classical music.

I cannot tell you what it is about classical music that makes it an important part of the Jailbird Diet. Thoreau didn't much care for it. "In Thoreau's eyes, concert music suffers from an over-cultivation, it has been domesticated. It has lost its spontaneity, vitality, and, most importantly, its affinity with life, i.e. nature." "'There is Music in Every Sound': Thoreau's Modernist Understanding of Music," Jannika Bok, https://copas.uni-regensburg.de/article/view/85/109.

I can only tell you that classical music allows the brain and the body to be more at rest and, therefore, deal more effectively with the reduction in food and caloric intake; listening to classical music while I walked made my walking more enjoyable and my dieting more bearable.

I make the same distinction between classical music and pop, hip-hop, rap, and oldies as I do the distinction between gossip and news. Again, not in the pejorative sense that Thoreau distinguished between the two; just in the sense that one is better suited for the sustaining of a short-term weight loss program than the other. As I work to maintain my weight loss in the free world, I continue to listen to my classical play list throughout my morning walks then switch up to my oldies play list in the afternoon. While this seems to be working for my maintenance program, I don't recommend it for severe weight loss; in my view, that requires classical throughout your walk schedule. While I do distinguish between music genres, I am unclear as to the incorporation of podcasts or books-on-tape into the walk playlists. The BOP did not allow prisoners to download podcasts or audio books, so this was not an option and, therefore, remains a question mark for me.

I did not appreciate all classical music equally. While I would rarely move away from WRTI during its classical music programming (which ended at 6:00 P.M. switching over to Jazz), there were classic music genres I particularly did not care for. I know less about classical music than I know about the science of dieting so bear with me.

Anything with harp and flute, and particularly harp and flute together, was not for me. I stayed away from piano concertos (though I do have some in my playlist, see below) while I enjoyed violin and cello concertos. I favored bigger symphonies over smaller quartets or chamber music. I could not tell a sonata from an etude but the bigger and bolder the symphonies the better. And I love Tchaikovsky. Anything Tchaikovsky. Any time Tchaikovsky. I downloaded only three music selections to my MP3, all Tchaikovsky: Swan Lake, Romeo and Juliet, and Scheherazade. Toward the end of each day at camp, when I was walking over ten miles a day and, therefore, on the track between 7:00 P.M. and 8:30 P.M., I would listen to one or all of these tracks over and over again.

Because I can't tell you why this happens, I will give you my new playlist (which I put together via Spotify during my first day of freedom). This playlist defines the type of classical music I would gravitate toward during my prison stay. Perhaps you will unlock the mystery behind the connection between the music choices I made and weight loss I achieved. If not, at the end of this section, I have pulled together some popular theories around classical music and its relation to weight loss.

Beethoven

The 5 Piano Concertos
Beethoven Symphonies 1–9

Mozart

Snippiness

Bach

#1 Bach
Two Hands

Tchaikovsky Compilation Including the Following:

The Nutcracker
Romeo and Juliet
Swan Lake
The Seasons
Eugene Onegin
Serenade for Strings in C; 048
Slavonic March, Op.31
Romance in F. Minor, Op.5
Symphony No. 2 in C Minor, Op. 17
Symphony No. 4 in F Minor, Op. 36
Symphony No. 5 in E Minor, Op. 64
The Queen of Spades, Op. 68
Pezzo Cappriccioso for Cello and Orchestra, Op. 62

Prokofiev

Romeo and Juliet
Cinderella

Rimsky-Korsakov

Scheherazade

Berlioz

Symphonie Fantastique

Copland
Super Hits

Mahler

Symphony No. 5 in C Sharp Minor
Symphony No. 9

Gershwin

Rhapsody in Blue

Debussy

La Mer and this Jeux

Haydn

Trumpet Concertos

Debussy, Faure and Ravel

String Quartets

Rachmaninov

Piano Concertos
Chants D'est
Dvorak
Complete Symphonies

During my home confinement, my daughter Phoebe turned me onto the soundtrack of Mozart in the Jungle – a streaming mini-series produced by Amazon. This is as good a Super Food as any music curated on WRTI.

Chapter 9
Super "Foods:" Plating Plato

I aspire to be acquainted with wiser men than this our Concord soil has produced, whose names are hardly known here. Or shall I hear the name of Plato and never read his book? As if Plato were my townsman and I never saw him – my next neighbor and never heard him speak or attended to the wisdom of his words. But how actually is it? His Dialogues, which contain what was immured in him, lie on the next shelf, and yet I never read them. We are underbred and low-lived and illiterate; and in this respect I confess I do not make any very broad distinction between the illiterateness of my townsmen who cannot read at all and the illiterateness of him who has learned to read only what is for children and feeble intellects. We should be as good as the worthies of antiquity, but partly by first knowing how good they were. We are a race of titmen, and soar but little higher in our intellectual flights than the columns of the daily paper.

Walden, p. 60

While the largest bloc of my time each day was spent walking and listening to music – from a minimum of three hours a day when I began my journey to a maximum of six hours when my journey came to an end – the second largest bloc of time was devoted to reading.

I had forgotten the joy of reading. I think I first abandoned recreational reading in law school when reading was devoted to torts, contracts, and criminal procedure. Then with kids, reading was nursery rhymes through to Harry Potter. With the explosion of streamed content both on television and online, reading became reduced to newspapers and online political sources. I had a number of books on my bedside table, I read them sparingly.

In prison, I became a reading machine.

I didn't start with Walden. That would not be shipped to me until my third week inside. I started with Charles Dickens's Bleak House. I actually started with Papillion – a book that had arrived the day I surrendered – but put it down after the first chapter; my mind was simply not prepared to read the story of a man wrongly accused rotting in prison. I never picked it up and to this day have still not read it (perhaps part of my own toxic purge).

Which is the first lesson of reading during your journey. As you have abandoned all the toxins of television, internet, and relationships, your world becomes filled with the men and women on the pages of the books with whom you have chosen to share your days. Books are a super food precisely because, if chosen wisely, they can on some level fill the void created by your toxin removal program.

And this is where I fear I will lose some of you. For I am convinced that not all reading provides the nutrients necessary to sustain short-term weight loss. Not all books are Super Foods.

In my second week at camp I saw a paperback on my neighbor's bed. It's title, Money, Mayhem, and Murder. It's author, Jihad. After asking around the White car, I found out that there was an entire genre of non-fiction of which I was totally unaware; one that did not make the New York Times Book Review. This genre is the Hood Novel.

Hood novels are as ubiquitous in the Black car section of the housing unit as the novels of Clive Cussler, James Patterson, or Tom Clancy are in the White car. I soon got my hands on my first hood novel, reading it in the housing unit while I read Bleak House in the park. In the first chapter of my hood novel, Dirty Divorce I, the female protagonist wife of a drug lord, is vaginally and anally raped by a rival drug lord. At the time of the rapes, her husband is fucking her best friend ergo the grounds for her seeking a divorce – and this was all in the first chapter!

I do not make much of a distinction between hood novels and Patterson's Alex Cross series, Cussler's Dirk Pitt or Clancy's Jason Bourne. They are all driven by two dimensional heroes and villains; like watching a Marvel adventure on the big screen – there may be some play between Iron Man and Pepper Pots but Stan Lee and the modern-day movie studios are far more about Character Generated Images than character development.

In the same way I distinguish between classical music and Hip-Hop, Rap, Country Western, Pop, or Reggae, I distinguish between classic literature and all other reading. Reading as a SuperFood was and is for me reading primarily classic literature. Just as Thoreau distinguished reading Plato from reading the current best sellers, I too make the same distinction. That is not to say I read only fiction in prison. Friends sent me plenty of non-fiction. Some of it was riveting, most notably "Say Nothing: A True Story of Murder and Memory in Northern Ireland" by Patrick Redden Keefe – a page-turning insiders look into the rise and compromise of the Irish Republican Army, and "Hero of the Empire: The Boer War, a Daring Escape, and the Making of Winston Churchill" which really does prove the adage, "truth can be stranger than fiction." But from my limited experience, non-fiction, no matter how compelling, did not do for my brain what great fiction did; it did not engage my mind in a way that it consumed me. That feeling of being consumed by the words on a page, for me, was reserved to great fiction.

Before I drill down into the nature of this super "food," I would be remiss if I didn't speak to one work of non-fiction that proved the exception to the rule. It does so because, I believe, it is written in the first person singular and brings a depth to character development that rivaled the best of non-fiction classics. *Educated* by Tara Westover. The author's metamorphosis from the child of a fire-breathing Evangelist father to a Harvard educated young woman rivals that of Meheude in Emile Zola's *Germinal* (read them and see for yourself). Does this mean that autobiographies as a genre are an exception to the classic-fiction-as super-food-rule? I cannot tell as *Educated* was the only autobiography I read in prison.

Educated reads like a work of great fiction precisely because it allows the reader to wander into the minds of the protagonist; to wrestle with the feelings and emotions of the cast as the cast wrestles with them; to be drawn into the love and hate, pleasure and pain, fear and confidence as events unfold. Classic literature is a super "food" for the very reason it is classic; the genre's first-person narratives are timeless and their timelessness means they connect to the same emotions and feelings of their nineteenth and twentieth century contemporaries as they do with, say, a camper languishing in a twenty-first century American prison.

While no other works of non-fiction made it onto my Super Foods list, there were two such books that did move me and I would feel remiss if I did not point them out. Both are in the same genre so I feel that this is more about me than some Super Food-like brain trigger so take them as such: Stephanie

Madoff's nightmare accounting of the fall of the House of Madoff in "The End of Normal" and Carly Simon's memories of her friendship with Jackie O in "Touched by the Sun."

Which leads me to a curious conundrum. *Walden*, as you by now have gathered, had a profound effect upon me; it created the very paradigm in which I lived my life and lost my weight for my ten months of incarceration; the vey paradigm that drives this book. But *Walden* was not, for me, a super "food." It did not trigger my brain and emotions the way the classic literature of Tolstoy or Dostoyevsky, Dickens or Gogol, Steinbeck or Hemingway, Heller of Irving did. I did not read it cover to cover. I skipped or skimmed over parts of little interest to me (this is even more ironic as the parts of least interest were those about food – the crops he planted and food he ate). I didn't make it through the first ten pages of his transcendentalist mentor's, *The Essential Writings of Ralph Waldo Emerson*. Thoreau writes of Plato's *The Republic* – I didn't care for it. I only passingly jumped through Aristotle's *Nicomachean Ethics*. Philosophic treatises, while considered classics, do not for me fall into the genre that makes them super "foods;" as the world of non-fiction, they did not trigger the chemical response in my brain and body that allowed me to move through my days free from hunger.

Which left for me the elephant in the room. Elephants I should say: the works considered the most classic of classic literature, the Koran and the Old and New Testament – all of which I read or attempted to read in prison.

I asked Shelly to send a copy of the Koran into Fairton when I was in my third month of incarceration. There was a small but strong Muslim car led by my so-called (for purposes of this writing only) Imam who I was now working with in food service. I figured reading the Koran would give me both better insight into the Muslim car and a nice gift for the Imam when I was done with it. While I kept the books I was currently reading either on the floor next to my bed (once I moved to a lower bunk) or on top of my bed during the day, I always kept the Koran under my bed and out of sight; I wasn't really sure how the White car would take to my reading of Muslim scripture.

I was disappointed. I thought I would be getting a series of stories on the rise of Muhammed and the creation of the Islamic religion. What I took from it was a dark, depressing world-view filled with rules and regulations covering everything from food and beverage consumption to copulation; a vengeful God and his prophets exacting ruination and hellfire for disobedience of the rules

72

and demanding conversion as absolution for Jews and Christians alike for their betrayal of Allah. The stories were few and far between; the most colorful of which involved the consequences of disobedience and what would happen to the fallen in Hell. I will say, the scripture did help inform me as the misogynistic currents running through the Koran created some of the most lively discussions in the kitchen between the Imam and the one regular female kitchen cop, Miss C – who I pegged as a Southern Baptist – when it came to the subject of the relationship between husband and wife in a Muslim household. Still, I only made it through a third of the Koran before I gave my present to the Imam.

As disappointing as the Koran was, I was equally underwhelmed with the Old and New Testament – a disappointment felt more profoundly as I was raised in a Jewish household that had me going to Hebrew School well beyond my Bar Mitzvah.

I hadn't planned on reading the Bible at camp. I had a pretty full list of classic literature on my plate by the time I was called to pack out in my tenth month. But the call to pack out had taken me by surprise; while lists of campers had been sent over to the medium security prison across the service road from the camp to undergo "isolation" before being released into the free, but Covid-Infected world, I had already received my out-date (the date in which campers have either served their maximum sentence or are sent to home confinement or a halfway house) before the pandemic hit and thought I would just stay in the camp until that date arrived. So when I was called to pack out, I did so in a hurry, leaving most of my books behind. Isolation, we were told, meant solitary confinement in a cell in the medium security prison. We were further told that we would not be returning to the camp after confinement so that everything we wanted to take from the camp would have to fit in mesh laundry bags and carried by us to the Medium. This meant ditching most of my books at the camp before heading off to the Medium. But when I got to the Medium, I was told by the cop that I had to leave most of my stuff in R&D (Receipt and Discharge) and take with me only toiletries, one change of clothes (we would be provided other clothing once inside) and a limited number of personal items. I took my notebooks and pens and one book, the Short Stories of Joseph Conrad.

When I got into the cell which, we were told was to be solitary isolation, I met my roommate (as so often happens in the BOP there is internal miscommunication which only ends up hurting prisoners; it happens so much that one begins to think it is part of the penalization program; leading to the BOP – Broken on Purpose – mindset).

What the BOP didn't get wrong was that isolation meant just that – locked in a cell 24/7 for the next 14 days. I now realized that I would not have enough reading material to last me. For me this was like the feeling a Tour de France rider must have when he is looking at Alpe Duez in the distance and reaches for his protein gel packs on the back of his jersey to find that they are all gone. I did the only thing I knew that would work. Started banging on the cell door and asking for the chaplain.

[Aside: Religion has a sacrosanct place in the incarcerated world. I found this out the first hour of my camp stay. A prisoner, let's call him Monty, comes up to me, hands me a piece of paper and tells me that I need to write the word Jew on it and sign my name (I guess it's obvious by my name that I am Jewish but it's not like a wore a Star of David on my sleeve as I walked into the camp). He told me that by doing so, I would get special meals and off-days during Yom Kippur and Rosh Hashanah, and every Friday get a piece of challah and some grape juice. Sounded like a no-brainer so I signed up for the Jew car.

A couple weeks later, a rabbi shows up at the camp. Russian M rounds up the Jews to go to the administrative trailer to meet with the rabbi. We pull our chairs into a circle with the rabbi at which point the rabbi, who has been here before, notices that Monty is missing. He asks CrapGame to go find Monty who goes and, upon returning, informs the rabbi that Monty refuses to come. And Monty was the guy who signed me up for the Jew car!

Then the rabbi begins to wrap tefillin – cubic black leather boxes with leather straps that Orthodox Jewish men wear on their head and strap around their arms and fingers during weekday morning prayer; observant Jews consider wearing tefillin to be a commandment of God. Now the last time I had stepped foot into a synagogue on my own (other than for the wedding of a friend's daughter or funerals of friends' parents) was twenty years ago. I, like so many of my American Jewish brethren of similar age and background, abandoned the religiosity of Judaism while remaining committed to its Zionism. I particularly abandoned the traditions which I found to be akin to the hocus pocus of a magic trick; for me there was no more hocus pocus in Judaism than the wrapping of tefillin. When it came my turn, I respectfully declined the offer. The story comes full circle when I find that my cell-mate in isolation is an observant Eastern European Jew who, you guessed it, wrapped tefillin every morning we were together in isolation.]

The chaplain brought me a rather small, soft-bound copy of the Bible.

So here's my take on the Bible and why, for me, it does not constitute a Super Food. The Old and New Testaments paint one-dimensional characters acting in a world of an equally one-dimensional God. There is little if any character development even in the stories that have some pretty amazing characters. Samson and Delilah, Noah, Job all have the depth of stick figures; the God of these scriptures is no less petulant and mercurial than that of the Koran. And in a prison world where the petulance and mercurialness of authoritarian figures is taken to an art form, the last thing I needed was to spend my time reading about another. Jesus and John, the Baptist are presented in far greater depth by Max von Sidow and Charleton Heston in the 1965 movie classic, The Greatest Story Ever Told, than they are in the New Testament. The Gospels in retelling the same story was like watching Ground Hog Day. I felt fortunate that the version of the Bible I was given had one-line headers on each page that summarized the pages text; I flew through Leviticus as it was a compilation of laws very reminiscent of the passages I found to be so painful to read in the Koran.

Perhaps a person absent of faith reads these scriptures in a way that takes away their ability to become super foods. Perhaps faith is what paints the multi-dimensional nature of the protagonists in a way that Gogol paints Chichikov in "Dead Souls," Dostoyevsky paints Smerdyakov in the Brothers Karamazov, Hemingway paints Harry in the "Snows of Kilimanjaro" or Irving paints John Wheelwright in "a Prayer for Owen Meany." I believe I learned far more about good and evil reading Zola's "Germinal" or Steinbeck's "Grapes of Wrath"; far more about faith in Steinbeck's, the Pearl;" far more about hope and despair in Tolstoy's "War and Peace" and far more about the human spirit in Conrad's, "The Secret Sharer" than I learned in any of the religious scriptures I read.

[Aside: This leads me to one final note about reading the classics; one that I only memorialize here because I felt it important enough to write down in my prison journal. It is a line of thinking that was sparked by a newspaper story I read early on about the lack of religious faith of Millennials and their abandonment of organized religion.

Caution: to some this will read as blasphemy.

There is so much great literature, classic literature, that informs us of the human condition in ways, to my mind, far more powerful than the words of Scripture. The examples I have given above are but just a few taken from my limited exploration of classic texts. There are thousands that I will never read, each I am confident, equally impactful, equally insightful, equally capable of placing the reader in greater touch with the human spirit. Yet people go to churches, synagogues, and mosques every week to read the same passages from the same texts interpreted and re-interpreted over and over and over again in much the same way to make them relevant to the modern experience.

Why not rethink organized religion into a book club on steroids? Gather on Sundays to discuss the works of the greatest writers that humankind has produced. Why not treat these great writers, whose works have lasted for generations and generations in the absence of an organized religion to prop them up, with no less deference and reverence than the gospels, greatest of Rabbis, or most learned of Imams?

What if on any given Saturday or Sunday, we could walk into a building that housed the book club and instead of a priest, rabbi, or imam on the stage, we heard from an English professor, librarian, theologian, or philosopher taking us through the texts of Pushkin, Dickens, or Hardy?

Had I spent the number of hours I spent in synagogue from age 10 to 18 being introduced to great literature rather than praying in Hebrew (a language I did not even understand), I am quite confident I would have a better understanding of, and perhaps belief in, an Almighty God than I do now.

Oh, and after book club is finished, throw in a three-mile walk or yoga class, followed by a healthy meal. Now that's an organized religion even I could devote myself to. But I digress.]

The following list are all the fiction and non-fiction titles I read during my ten months of incarceration. While this is entirely a collection of Western literature, I see no reason why the works of Mahdi, Ibn Khalduin, or Salih or the Water Margin, Journey to the West, Romance of the Three Kingdoms, or Dream of the Red Chamber – the so-called "Four Classics of Chinese Literature" – cannot perform the same super food role in your diet.

My reading list is set down here chronologically by date read (first being earliest) and is annotated by fiction (F) and non-fiction (NF) with Super Foods are in **Bold**:

Bleak House, Charles Dickens (curiously, perhaps ironically, the only Dickens work in the Fairton library) (F)

The Sun Also Rises, Ernest Hemingway (F)

A Little History of the World, E.H. Gombrich (NF)

Ned Kelly: A Notorious Bandit of the Australian Outback, Peter Carey(F)

Sapiens: A Brief History of Humankind, Yuval Noah Harari (NF)

Gods of the Upper Air, Charles King (NF)

Dirty Divorce Part 1, Miss KP (F)

Hero of the Empire: The Boer War, a Daring Escape, and the Making of Winston Churchill, Candace Millard (F)

Educated, Tara Westover (NF)

Where the Crawdads Sing, Delia Owens (F)

The Brothers Karamazov, Fyodor Dostoevsky (F)

Chance Are, Richard Russo (F)

Walden, Henry David Thoreau (NF)

The Essential Writings of Ralph Waldo Emerson, Ralph Waldo Emerson(NF).

The Cockroach, Ian McEwan

The Republic, Plato (NF)

Nicomacean Ethics, Aristotle (NF)

House of Usher, Edgar Allen Poe (F)

War and Peace, Leo Tolstoy (F)

Destination Moon, Seymour Simon (NF)

To Kill the Irishman: The war That Crippled the Mafia, Rick Porello (NF)

The Last of the Mohicans, James Fenimore Cooper (F)

Destiny of the Republic: A Tale of Madness, Medicine, and the Murder of a President, Candace Millard (NF)

The Beneficiary, Janney Scott (NF)

The Overstory: A Novel, Richard Powers (F)

Noble Quran, Dr. Taqi-ud-Din Al Hilali

Dubliners, James Joyce (F)*

History of the World in Six Glasses, Tom Standage (NF)

The Short Novels of John Steinbeck, John Steinbeck (F)

Includes:

Tortilla Flats, The Moon is Down, The Red Pony, Of Mice and Men, Cannery Row, and The Pearl

Selected Stories of Anton Chekov, Anton Chekov (F)
The Complete Short Stories of Ernest Hemingway, Ernest Hemingway (F)
City of Thieves, David Benioff (F)**
American Dirt: A Novel, Jeanine Cummins (F)
King Lear, William Shakespeare (F)***
Macbeth, William Shakespeare (F)
Hamlet, William Shakespeare (F)
Change Your Brain, Change Your Life, Daniel G. Amen (NF)
Born A Crime, Trevor Noah (NF)
Fountainhead, Ayn Rand (F)
Shantaram, Gregory David Roberts (F)****
Say Nothing: A True Story of Murder and Memory in Northern Ireland, Patrick Radden Keefe (NF)
Grapes of Wrath, John Steinbeck (F)
Evicted: Poverty and Profit in the American City, Matthew Desmond (NF)
The End of Normal, Stephanie Madoff (NF)
The Deerslayer, James Fenimore Cooper (F)
Lucky 666, Jailbird Diet Drury and Tom Clavin (NF)
A Prayer for Owen Meany, John Irving (F)*****
Germinal, Emile Zola (F)******
Catch-22, Joseph Heller, (F)
Dead Souls, Nikolai Gogol (F)
O. Henry 41 Stories: 150th Anniversary Edition, O. Henry (F)
Atlas Shrugged, Ayn Rand (F)
Touched By the Sun: My Friendship with Jackie, Carly Simon
A Midsummer Night's Dream, William Shakespeare, (F)
Mountain Shadow, Gregory David Roberts (F)
The Great Inspector, Nikolai Gogol (F)
Nutshell: A Novel, Ian McEwan (F)
Holy Bible, King James Version
Heart of Darkness and Selected Short Fiction, Joseph Conrad (F)

* While I found *Dubliners* thoroughly enjoyable, I found Joyce's classic *Ulysses* unintelligible. I tried on three separate occasions to read it and could not get through the fifth chapter on my last read. Perhaps it is me but if reading a book requires Cliff's Notes (old school reference I realize) to understand even the most basic of who is doing what to whom, it's not worth my time. The world is filled with classic literature I can understand.

** *City of Thieves* marks one of only three books of fiction not considered classics that I considered to be a Super "Food." The others are Ian McEwan's, *Nutshell* and Richard Power's *The Overstory: A Novel.* All moved me in ways all super food reading does.

*** You cannot go wrong putting Shakespeare – any Shakespeare – on your Super Food reading list. But if you do, I suggest you get a version with a side-by-side modern English rendition such as No Fear Shakespeare or those edited by S.J. Hill.

**** I had never heard of *Shantaram* or its sequel, *Mountain Shadow*, until at camp; The Big I implored me to read it. It was perhaps the greatest gift any camper bestowed upon me during my time being down. These sweeping sagas of modern-day India captured my heart and imagination. They are the most super of super "foods." Be warned – you will put traveling to Mumbai on your bucket list once you've read them.

***** If there is one book you read before you die, read *A Prayer for Owen Meany.* Period.

****** *Germinal* was the third book I found in the Fairton library that made it onto the Super Foods reading list. The first was Dickens's *Bleak House* which I checked out my first day at camp (yes, this library had a check out system and librarian, Schneider, who was a stickler for checking books out though not so much for their return) and *A Prayer for Owen Meany* which I happened to see one night just sitting alone atop the library room copier.

I found Zola's *Germinal* to be strikingly similar to Steinbeck's Grapes of Wrath, which I had completed just a couple weeks earlier. I suggest you read them back-to-back as it will give you a great sense of the global nature and timelessness of the depravity of class discrimination and the hopefulness of self-determination.

A few last thoughts about those that made it onto the list.

I devoured Hemingway's short stories but didn't care so much for those based on his war time experience. I did not read For Whom the Bells Toll which may have changed my view on this.

I thought Heller's Catch-22 was a bit of a one-trick pony but the trick – the situational inanity and the dialogue which described it – was such a great one that it became like watching a demolition derby waiting for the crashes.

While Heart of Darkness gets most of the Joseph Conrad attention, I cherish three of his other short stories: Youth, Amy Foster, and The Secret Sharer. The same can be said for me when it comes to Steinbeck: I read Grapes of Wrath in prison and East of Eden before prison but I fell in love with his short novels, The Pearl and Cannery Row.

As with music, I do not understand the chemical reaction that reading classic literature has in the brain or body that leads it to becoming a super food capable of curbing appetite and a cessation of hunger even in the face of a drastic daily reduction of calories. As with music, I apply the pornography rule of Justice Stevens – you know it as a super food when you read it.

Chapter 10
Super "Foods:" Cross-Wording

I didn't start really doing crossword puzzles until I was in my forties. I never did them in high school or college; dabbled with them a bit as a way to kill time in some boring law school classes; then started to focus more seriously on them when I started my New York Times subscription in the late 1990s.

It was my grandmother, Mildred Lasch, who spurred my interest in puzzling. She was an avid cross-worder till the very end of her days. I would travel into the city each week to her apartment where we would complete the Sunday Times crossword together – I would read her the clues, the number of letters, and those that we had filled in, and she would work out the solutions.

I came to camp prepared. I had daily subscriptions to the Wall Street Journal and New York Times which gave me two daily cross-wording opportunities (WSJ combines Saturday and Sunday into a bigger weekend puzzle which I pegged at a Thursday-Friday NYT degree of difficulty.). On top of these daily puzzles, I had Shelly send in three crossword compilations: The NYT Sunday Crossword Compilation, Volume 11, NYT Ferocious Crosswords, and NYT Tough Crossword Omnibus, Volume 1.

I am not one for other non-crossword type puzzles with the exception of the NYT Sunday Spelling Bee and, on rare occasions the NYT Sunday Smart Set. I never attempted Cryptic Crosswords or Anagrams and Puns. I was not a KenKen or Sudoku player. For me, it was crosswords.

I do crosswords in pen not because I am so confident in my ability but because I would rather draw over a wrong answer in pen than degrade the paper with an eraser. While I am somewhat competent at all levels of the daily crosswords, I struggle mightily at the hardcore omnibus puzzles. In these, I cheat regularly on proper nouns looking at the answer grid trying to disclose to myself just the word I am looking for and no other. I don't lose sleep because

I failed to know "Memed My Hawk" director and star, 1984, seven letters, (answer: Ustinov), Brian of "Juarez", 1939, six letters, (answer: Aherne), or Playwright/painter Wyspianski, nine letters, (answer: Stanislaw). I am not proud of cheating in these but I do feel I am getting better for it (and needing to cheat less).

Crosswords in the park. Crosswords in my bed. Crosswords watching television. Crosswords filling every waking moment that I was not working, eating, walking, reading or in the bathroom. There was not a television show I watched, even Philadelphia Eagles games, that did not include cross-wording. I averaged three to four crosswords per day; the two daily puzzles and at least one of the omnibus puzzles. While the dailies would take minutes to an hour or more based upon the day's degree of difficulty, the omnibus' levels of difficulty required over an hour or better to complete. I figure that I completed over 1,000 crossword puzzles during my ten months stay at the camp.

I suspect that playing other games or solving other mental challenges will have the same effect in regulating hunger as crosswords. The millions of possible moves and outcomes in chess seems to replicate the search for words in a complex crossword puzzle. Chess was very popular in the chow hall between meals and late night. It is not, however, the slow contemplative game you might see in the park or in the movies (or in the park in a movie, see *Charlie Wilson's War*). No, the prison version of chess is a fast-paced, make-your-move-with-loud-flourish, play with head phones on, in your face affair. If I had any designs on learning the game in prison, they were dashed the first time I saw this angst-ridden sped-up version.

But chess is flawed as a substitute for cross-wording in the Jailbird Diet because 1. It requires a partner and some level of social interaction – two things that are anathema to the diet; 2. The level of difficulty and, therefore, challenge, is pegged to the ability of your opponent, again an outside input discouraged in a diet based upon the principle of solitude retooling your mind; and 3. I'm not sure you can play chess and watch television at the same time.

This last differential is most important. Cross-wording is an important component of the Jailbird Diet because it allows you to layer it over another brain activity. It is the layering that creates the mindset in which hunger is removed. I had no problem watching any live sporting event while cross-wording. I found the local and national news to be unwatchable without a crossword in hand. And I had no problem cross-wording while watching the two drama series television shows I did watch while inside: USA Network's *Queen of the South* and TNT's *Animal Kingdom*.

[A note about these two shows. It was rare that the Black TV and White TV ever shared the same content. These two shows were the exception. That both involved strong female leads, Ellen Barkin as "Smurf," the matriarch of a dysfunctional crime family in *Animal Kingdom* and Alice Braga as Teresa Mendoza in *Queen of the South*, head of a South American drug cartel relocating to New Orleans, speaks volumes (and I am sure would make for an interesting sociological paper for another time and another author). These shows were so popular that they played twice each night back-to-back. As they came on at 9:00 P.M., we would invariably be called back into the housing unit for count 45 minutes into each episode (for the nightly 10 P.M. count). So when we returned to the chow hall after the count, we would watch the rerun that started at 10:00 just so we could catch the last 20 minutes we had missed.]

I cannot stress the importance of crosswords to my weight loss program. I credit cross-wording more than any other factor with giving me the willpower to not succumb to the temptations of the carbo-palooza.

Do not let the difficulty of crosswords stand in your way. I am encouraging my kids to crossword. Not as a weight loss tool but as a mind-sharpening exercise. They have the Tuesday NYT Omnibus. We have done Monday crosswords together. Begin with the easiest ones you can find and build from there. Crosswords, you will find, have their own tricks. They are limited primarily to words of less than seven characters with multiple vowels. Because of these limits, clues and answers repeat themselves: places like the World War II battlefield, STLO, Australian animal, EMU, and popes, LEO (pick any Roman numeral under XIV) are just a few you will learn as you go.

As I mainly did cross-wording during TV hours evenings in the chow hall, at the height of the carbo-palooza when all around me was junk food prep and junk food consumption, layering onto my brain another activity beyond the more passive television viewing, was just the distraction I needed. But more than a distraction, it seemingly took away my desire for the food all around me; it took the hunger out of me.

There is no literature – science, pseudo-science, or other – that provides a link between cross-wording and weight loss. There is a line of commentary that equates the use of more brain power with a higher rate of burning calories but the incremental burn rate is minimal and that is not the place that cross-wording or any equally challenging brain activity plays in the Jailbird Diet. As a super "food," it conditions your mind and body for significantly lower caloric intake; that it did so at precisely the time I needed it most – the hours after the food service shut down at 4:30 to bedtime for me at 11:00 – made it the super "food" that replaced more junk food than any other. In the free world, if you do fill your post-dinner hours with television, even if in the most inane of forms, never watch without a crossword on your lap and pen in hand. I think you will find, as I did, that you can avoid the junk food cravings even when that food presents itself all around you.

Part II
Digging In

"There is a certain class of unbelievers who sometimes ask me such questions as, if I think I can live on vegetable food alone; and to strike at the root of the matter at once – for the root is faith – I am accustomed to answer such, that I can live on board nails. If they cannot understand that, they cannot understand much that I have to say. For my part, I am glad to hear of experiments of this kind being tried; as that a young man tried for a fortnight to live on hard, raw corn on the ear, using his teeth for all mortar. The squirrel tribe tried all the same and succeeded."

Walden, p. 37.

Ten chapters into the Jailbird Diet and we are finally getting to the subject of food. This is as it should be as this diet is far more about conditioning your mind, body, and soul for significant caloric deprivation than about the kind of calories that you ultimately decide to consume.

Before we do a deeper dive into food choices on the Jailbird Diet, let me make it clear from the outset of these chapters: this diet is not predicted upon your making the best food choices from a nutritional stand point. I chose to avoid the canned vegetables in prison because I did not like their taste and they carried too much sugar and starch. This left me with a diet devoid of key nutrients for ten months. While I tried to replace these nutrients with commissary-bought vitamin supplements, I am sure any nutritionist will tell you that I was losing out in the exchange.

You can lose weight on this diet regardless of the foods you accept into your daily meal plan. There is no counting calories on this diet but you can count them if you want to. Take the food logs in the Appendix as a guide and you will succeed as I did.

I did not choose to abstain from alcohol, that decision was made for me by the BOP. Of course, I could have gotten around this by engaging the Lefts and

Washington (see Chapter 19, "What left left") of the camp to make a contraband run for me, but I chose not to.

The prohibition on alcohol removes a potentially significant amount of calories from one's daily intake. Take out cocktail hours, weekend binges, nightcaps and you will quickly remove large amounts of calories from your weekly diet. But removal of one potential calorie load does not mean that this load cannot be easily replaced by a load that is not considered contraband. One inmate consumed large amounts of chocolate on a daily basis. When asked how it was that he could eat so much chocolate and seemingly not gain any weight in prison his response, "My daily chocolate of choice on the outside was a fistful of scotch."

So if you want to put alcohol into your diet, have at it. But you can't have your alcohol and your candy. Add alcohol, take away snacks. Or take away dinner. At times, I ate an entire serving of ice cream at lunch. On those rare occasions, the ice cream was all I ate for lunch. So you want to eat ice cream for lunch, have at it. The Jailbird Diet will give you the ability to make these bad food choices as easily as it will allow you to make good food choices. Either way you will be consuming far less in volume and calories than you had before without feeling hungry. Either way you will achieve the ultimate goal – weight loss.

As you are about to see, the kitchen at Fairton closed at 4:30 P.M. – nothing you ate after 4:30 was coming from the BOP; there was no refrigerator to browse through in between TV shows. But in many ways at 4:30 P.M., when the kitchen was locked down and the kitchen cop clocked out for the day, the real eating – or what I came to call the Carbo-Palooza – was about to begin.

The stacked chairs came off the chow hall walls to create the TV Room, Jose came running in with the flour tortillas to do the prep for Nell's pizza concession, Larry started prepping the paella for the Spanish car, Tabby and Shah prepping for the black car, the Muslim car started making chicken curry and Pad Thai and the White car in the corner began to build their strombolis. More calories were consumed outside kitchen hours as were consumed in the three daily meals provided by the BOP.

In many ways, the proof that mind and body can be conditioned to not experience hunger was borne out in the hours I spent each night in the chow hall outside of meal times; hours in which there was snacking in every direction I turned and none of it seemed to matter to me. Again, while prison can create a unique environment for weight loss it can equally create the perfect environment for weight gain.

Chapter 11
Feeding Time at the Zoo

Launching a weight loss program in a federal prison is, in many ways, much easier than launching one in the free world. Incarceration in a federal prison is like being at a fat camp directed by Timothy Burton. There are rules established by the Bureau of Prisons that make a significant, sustained weight loss program much, much easier than undertaking one in the free world. None more significant than the eating schedule.

The schedule, one quickly comes to understand, is pegged to the work schedule of the kitchen cop and the afternoon count schedule. The kitchen cop clocked in to work by 7:00 A.M., unlocked the kitchen door, oversaw all aspects of lunch, dinner, and the next day's breakfast preparation, locked the kitchen back up at 4:30, and clocked out. The lunch and dinner windows were set to accommodate this schedule allowing the BOP to assign one cop all of the kitchen duties each day rather than have these responsibilities shared across two kitchen cop work shifts. The ridiculously early dinner schedule also accommodated the 4:00 P.M. count as the kitchen served two dinner lines: the early or "Short Line" queued up at 3:00 P.M. so that early diners were finished in time for 3:45 recall to bunks for the 4:00 P.M. count. The "Main Line" would then be served upon completion of the 4:00 P.M. count and run till the kitchen was locked up at 4:30.

While there are many aspects of prison life that take you far away from the routine of the free world, few will take you there faster than the prison dining schedule which replicates no schedule I had ever been part of in the free world. The last time my lunch window opened at 10:00 A.M. and my dinner window closed at 4:30 P.M., I was in diapers being spoon-fed mashed peas in a high chair.

It is not that the daily eating schedule becomes compressed, the time spent eating within this compressed schedule is compressed. The dining experience in the chow hall is more like cows feeding at a trough than social dining. Few spent more time at their tables than it took them to eat the food in front of them; no lingering over coffee and dessert discussing the events of the day; no discussions of work affairs over one more plastic cup of bug juice; no Animal House food fights; no high school drama. Just get your food, find your seat, sit, eat, bus your tray, goodbye.

What intermittent fasting enforces through its restrictive timeline is an absence of social dining which is also absent in prison life. I cannot recall one meal in the chow hall ever lasting for me more than 15 minutes. I did not engage in lengthy conversations over food with anyone at my table – ever. I came, I saw, I ate. Period. The total time per day I devoted to eating in a federal prison came in well under 30–45 minutes.

Chapter 12
Table for Four

The dining room, commonly referred to as the chow hall, was where most of the men spent most of their waking hours indoors. It was a rectangular room much like your high school cafeteria: 20 rectangular four-top industrial tables each with a metal base out of which extended four mushroom cap seats with a plastic table top. These stretched in three rows the length of the room; an additional three 2-tops attached to the western wall; three free standing tables – two at the western wall, one at the southern wall; two moveable cafeteria galley units for serving hot and cold food and a table for the water/juice bar against the east wall.

The tables, like everything else in the camp including bunks and toilets, were allocated by race which replicated the television viewing areas which also were allocated by race. From the double doors leading into the chow hall, the White tables were congregated in the near right corner above which the White TV sat 8' off the floor against the west wall. The other enclave of White tables was in the far-right corner by the Sports TV which stood 8' off the floor against the south wall. The Spanish tables lined up across three rows in front of the Spanish TV down the west wall from the White TV. The Black tables took up the last block of tables toward the south of the room lined up by the Black TV on the far west wall and the Sports TV on the south wall.

There was a Muslim table in the Black section; the Indian sub-continent Muslims had a table; the transgender camper had a two-top against the west wall.

While there were no assigned seats in the chow hall there were assigned seats in the chow hall; assigned by seniority where the senior most members of the table called the shots as to the replacement for a dining member who packed out. Chow hall seating assignments were treated with the same deference as personal property; you didn't sit in another camper's spot without getting his approval; if you were sitting there, let's say, for the Short Line meal thinking the seat's owner was not eating till the Main Line, and the owner showed, you got up – and apologized. And so decorum reigned in the chow hall. Like so much at camp, these rules of engagement, while sounding somewhat restrictive in the free world, were nowhere near as restrictive as they were in higher security facilities where not only race but geographic identity (Baltimore v. DC, NYC v. PHL) and gang affiliation dictated seating assignments and violations of the seating chart led to altercation and recrimination (or so I was told).

Connected to the chow hall on its eastern side was the library/computer room: six computer stations ringing two of its walls; bookshelves on one wall, a desk and copier against the remaining wall. In the middle of the room, a group of moveable bookshelves and a six-foot work table. The computers were in constant use for email purposes only (there is no Internet in prison) allowing prisoners 30 minutes of communication at a time to a BOP-approved list of recipients. At night, the moveable bookshelves were moved outside of the room into the chow hall to accommodate the repurposed use of the 6-foot table for black jack or poker – gaming that would go into the wee hours of the morning.

Next to the library/computer room was a room on the outside of which a sign read "Education Room." As you might have guessed, an education department that approves a scuba diving class for a prison without water, let alone any scuba diving equipment, is not really focused on education. In my ten months stay, the door to this room was opened no more than ten percent of the time. On those days, campers were doing some level of GED preparation yet I do not know of one camper passing his GED while I was there.

[Aside: This is one of the most depressing parts of the prison story. A camp like Fairton is the last stop for prisoners transitioning back into the free world. Yet the education is a joke, and not a good one. I never took an education course but my understanding of the course on Western Civilization was that it was really about the Vikings, the Business Enterprise class was really about using minority status to access federal contracts and Scuba was, well, about scuba. The men did not view their time in Fairton as time to prepare for life in the free world because Fairton did not view itself as anything more than a place for its campers to kill time waiting for their out date.]

On the free-standing tables at the west and north walls sat the microwaves. Every day of my camp experience, these microwaves were in constant use. As you will see later in this chapter, they were the bulwarks of the carbo-palooza that formed a large part of the camper diet.

Toward the end of my stay, I came to learn microwaves were no longer the rule but the exception in the federal prison system. In March 2020, nine months into my stay, the Camp Counselor announced that all the microwaves would be confiscated on the first of May. As the counselor knew full well the importance of these machines to the daily lives of the campers, the move seemed to me to be both unwarranted and somewhat Draconian. The microwaves were providing an important supplement to the camper diet and, as best as I could tell, were hurting no one. My experience taught me in my short stay that campers with full bellies were happier and more docile than those left to take their entire daily nutrition from what the kitchen served up. Surely, the BOP must know this as well.

But while the campers understood the adverse impact such a move would have on their food choices and the quality of their daily lives, they didn't seem particularly jarred by the confiscation notice. I quickly understood why. Campers coming down from higher security facilities knew full well why microwaves were banned in the BOP.

When I would tell my friends of the confiscation order, I would ask them this question: Why would the BOP take away microwaves that were clearly helping to keep the peace and hurting no one?

Their answers invariably came down to prisoners blowing something up in the microwave. And this shows two fundamental misunderstandings the free world has of the prisoner dynamic. First, prisoners would not blow up a machine that other prisoners found of value – such an act would run against the fundamental rules of personal property upon which orderly prison life is based: you don't destroy another prisoner's property and you certainly don't destroy property that all of the other prisoners use to make their lives a little bit more normal. Second, when you ask yourself why the BOP takes any pecuniary action, the answer will generally come down to this: what is the worst thing the BOP is trying to prevent by taking this action?

The worst act a prisoner could undertake with a microwave is not to use it as a bomb but to use its heating capability as a weapon. Take your commissary purchased bowl, add commissary purchased oil-based product (there is a reason commissaries do not sell baby oil though they do sell olive oil), add water, heat to boiling, then throw into the face of adversary; as happened in Fort Dix in a fight over a transvestite (or so I am told).

In the wake of the microwave ban, necessity will again become the mother of invention or in this case the mother of something called a "stinger": take two electric outlet plates, get your hands on an electrical cord and split the wire exposing the two ends, loop those ends through the hole in each of the two outlet plates and you are ready. Now take a mop bucket and fill it with water. Drop the plates into the bucket of water (making sure they do not touch!) and plug the cord into the wall socket. Now take your Ramen noodle pack, paella in your commissary bowl, or raw chicken in a bag (pick your poison) and place it in the bucket of water. Et Voila – a stinger! Or so I am told.

Chapter 13
Breakfast: Bagging Bran

Breakfast during the weekdays was entirely a solo affair. It was not hot and it was not served on the chow line. As the chow cop did not open up the kitchen until 7:00 A.M. – an hour when most campers were already up the road working their jobs, breakfasts were handed out in brown paper bags at the dinner chow line the day before. These bags would be taken by the campers to their lockers after dinner then retrieved the next morning and taken into the chow hall. Starting at 5:30 A.M., campers would walk down the concrete and cinderblock hallway that leads from the housing unit to the chow hall. Between 6:00 and 6:15, the housing unit cop would open up the kitchen allowing campers (most often Juice or, Murder Mike) to go to the refrigerator and take out two cases of non-fat milk 1/2 pints to put out into the chow hall. The unit cop would then lock the kitchen back up waiting for the kitchen cop to open it back up when he arrived at 7:00 A.M.

Campers would grab one, two, six milks (while campers are very respectful of personal property boundaries, they share no sense of sharing resources for the common good; as we have seen, the notion that one should only take enough milk for themselves thereby allowing every camper to get some was as foreign a concept to these campers as binomial equations on the GED exam. It was understood that campers would take for themselves, some for others who would pay them in mackerel to have their milk brought to their bunk other than have to wake up before 6:15 for it. This was understood and accepted. If you couldn't figure out how to get milk in the morning for yourself, then you didn't deserve the milk in the first place. If it was gone, that was on you and not on the camper who took ten milks out of the case.

So now you've got your milk, you've got your breakfast bag, your MP3 or radio (these provided audio for the four televisions on separate radio frequencies), and your headset – Dig In!

The breakfast bags included the following: one piece of fruit; a pastry; cold cereal (typically bran or corn flakes though apple cinnamon crunch did make an appearance one week); a packet of hot cereal (Farina or oatmeal) every other day, two pink packs of sugar substitute, and a mini throwaway spork.

The range of BOP fruit ran the gamut from fresh melon (in the summer months) to rotten apples and bananas (the rottenness of the bananas enhanced by the food service freezing and thawing which I am pretty sure is a banana no-no. Even so, bananas were a highly valued commodity in almost any color as they provided a source of potassium craved by the weight lifting crowd. Bananas commanded the attention of the underground market whether they were, green, yellow, or brown).

Apples were the most common breakfast fruit and were, for the most part, Red (and not so) Delicious. Pears if they were green were barely edible unless they were the Washington State brand which came in green and brown varieties and were fresh and crisp.

Two types of pastry hit the breakfast bags: pre-packaged and kitchen made. Like the fruit, pastry was hit and miss. The pre-packaged items ranged from Krispy Kreme honey buns to cinnamon oat scones (scones is what I called them; the campers called them "choke biscuits" describing what would occur if you ate them in the absence of milk. These pre-packaged delights became so ubiquitous some weeks that the men refused to eat them placing them in the public domain on the microwave tables like a pastry lost and found, See Chapter 8, Side Dishes). I never ate the breakfast pastry – and for good reason. The Krispy Kreme Honey Bun clocked in at 410 calories, 26 grams of fat, and 52 grams of carbohydrates.

In February, word came down from the food warehouse that the BOP had scored thousands upon thousands of muffins that Starbucks had put up for auction as they approached their expiration dates (or so I am told): blueberry and blueberry with cream cheese filling, cranberry, bran, pumpkin, corn, chocolate chip and chocolate chip with chocolate fudge, and banana walnut.

We also received one batch of lemon poppy muffins which became a BOP cautionary tale when two campers, each consuming one such muffin earlier in the day, tested positive for opiates in the nightly random drug screening later that evening. Apparently, the lemon poppy muffins had been pulled before they went into the Medium but that order had not made it down to the camp before some were distributed into the breakfast bags.

The Starbucks muffins were in the breakfast bags every week from the beginning of February to the middle of April when I packed out; they were in the breakfast bags that G and I received through the door in isolation.

I ate cold bran cereal every morning. My first days in prison, I ate the breakfast bag like a prisoner who didn't know any better. Eat the fruit, take a couple bites of the pastry, and eat my cereal and skim milk. To ensure enough bran cereal supply, I would trade out my pastry for extra cereal bags with my table mates.

I was the exception. Almost all the campers supplemented their breakfast with cereals purchased in commissary. The commissary had no shortage of hot and cold cereals. It also had a variety of coffee products none of which I consumed (In the free world, I was a Starbucks quad-shot espresso guy to which I would add a ridiculous amount of cream to fix myself a caffeine milkshake that I would sip throughout the mornings. I weaned myself of this habit in the months before I entered camp.).

So I wised up and started putting Raisin Bran onto my weekly commissary order and forgot about the breakfast bags altogether (if I liked the fruit I would save it for lunch, dinner, or snack). When I took the bran cereal from the breakfast bags, it was a dry, sugarless composition pre-packaged in a 1 and 1/3 cup container with a 110-calorie count. The 1/2 pint of milk carried 80 calories, leaving me at under 200 calories count for breakfast. These were the only calories I counted all day – only doing so because they were staring me in the face.

When I shifted to purchasing my Raisin Bran through commissary, it came in large plastic bags at 120 calories per serving with the bag containing a total of seven servings. I tried to make each bag last for seven days thereby replicating the calorie count of the pre-packaged cereal. That never worked out. My bag would usually last five days, meaning that my breakfast calorie count was jumping to 250–275 calories. I didn't think this would kill my diet and, as it turned out, it didn't.

I found this breakfast accomplished two important goals: first, the bran kept me feeling full well into the afternoon allowing me to limit my food consumption at the 10:30 lunch; second, the bran facilitated the movement of my bowels which, because of the very restrictive nature of my lunch and dinner menus, particularly in the absence of any vegetable or starch fiber, were not moving so frequently. For these reasons alone, breakfast became the most important meal of the day.

My first breakfast log was recorded June 24, 2019 – one week after my surrender. It reads: two bites pastry; apple; diet coke (12 packs of soda of all kinds were available for purchase at the commissary). The pastry was surprisingly tasty with a buttery, flakey crust and fruit-filled center. I loved them – two bites was real will power. The next day, June 25th: skim milk, half danish. The remainder of June through July 20th every breakfast was the same: bites of danish and a 1/2 pint of milk. On July 21, I introduced bran flakes to the breakfast menu. When I had a banana, it would go into the breakfast mix but that was more the exception than the rule. I put my commissary-bought peanut butter into a few of these breakfasts. But in these first weeks I found that my lunch and dinner programs were almost completely devoid of fiber the absence of which, combined with the sever reduction in food mass, led to days on end without moving my bowels. The breakfast transition to bran then Raisin Bran was, for me, a biological imperative – one supplemented by laxatives which I acquired through a trade of my commissary-bought Kosher chicken dinner with Norad, – my hypochondriacal chow table mate.

From August 9, 2019 to the day I packed out on April 16, 2020 every breakfast I ate recorded one 1/2-pint carton of skim milk and bran cereal or Raisin Bran. That was it. No more danish, no more peanut butter, bananas or any other fruit. Just milk and cereal.

I found the vitamins and nutrients provided by one and half cups of raisin bran and half pint of milk gave me the energy to walk allowing me to walk two and then three miles each morning; they also gave me the sense of fullness that pushed any sense of hunger off for hours. I did cheat at breakfast particularly when the Starbucks muffins hit the bags. I would scoop out and devour the cream cheese buried in the blueberry muffins and do the same with the chocolate fudge buried in the chocolate chip muffins. With the banana nut muffins, I would nibble away at the sugary top and discard the rest.

While every other meal was a rotating menu of whatever food service was providing or substituting in commissary purchased foods when the food serve menu was lacking, breakfast never varied; it was a guaranteed source of fiber and fullness that came in under 300 calories. It was also my favorite meal –

the one I looked forward to most the night before; the one I could always count on.

A bang on the cell door. The slot opens and two brown bags are placed through to my hands; then the two 1/2 pints of skim milk. Something I have never seen in a breakfast bag at camp – a large single serving of Cocoa Krispies (is it Throwback Thursday? – so hard to keep track of days when locked in a cell 24/7): 2.3 ounces, 250 calories, 58 grams of carbs, 28 grams of sugar. I take the apple and the sugar substitutes and ditch the Cocoa Krispies. Can't wait for lunch!

Chapter 14
Lunch: The Best Calories
Come in Small Packages

While breakfast bags were always like Gump's box of chocolates – you never knew what you were gonna get – lunch in the BOP is a far more predictable affair. Across all 120 BOP facilities there is a posted weekly meal calendar of lunches and dinners (or so I am told). Ours was posted just outside the kitchen door with a thumbtack denoting which weekly schedule we were following. On four out of five weekdays the same lunch menu carried across all institutions: Tuesday – chicken patty; Wednesday – burger and fries; Thursday – chicken quarter (leg and thigh); Friday – fish (fried or baked but always breaded – think a poor man's Mrs. Paul's).

The predictability of the lunch schedule was a real plus for diet execution as it allowed me to set my protein schedule in advance. While dinner (as we shall see in the next chapter) had its protein, it was typically mixed into a bean, noodle, rice, or gravy that carbed it up requiring protein extraction; lunch on the other hand delivered isolated protein.

But even so, lunch like every meal and snack, required some attention to detail. Tuesday's chicken and Friday's fish were breaded and fried, requiring a peel-n-eat approach to get the protein without the carbs. I did this religiously through the first seven months of my stay. By October 2019, I had ditched the Tuesday and Friday lunches; by January 2020 all my lunches were being used in my food hustle (See Part IX. Side Dishes, Chapter 1. Do the Hustle).

Institutionalized portion control kept my lunch calorie count to a bare minimum – whether I liked it or not. I found this out the hard way at my very first lunch meal.

My first lunch, June 18, 2019, was Chicken Patty Tuesday. As I went through the chow line, I replicated what those in front of me were doing –

placed my plastic tray on the metal top of the hot serve line to be taken down by the server filled and returned back to the top to be slid down to the next server. The protein always comes first to be followed by the carbs then the vegetables with bread at the end of the line. The server placed two chicken patties on the tray of the camper in front of me then slid it down the line for the potatoes and the canned peas and carrots beyond. The server, the Imam, then took my tray, placed one patty on it, then passed it down the line. One of the two Asians in the camp, Chino, was the next server down the line.

Now Silverman, a former Fairton camper who briefed me before I went in, told me that there was no such thing as seconds in the BOP chow line. But this was not technically seconds, more like doubling up firsts, so I asked Chino for a second patty. Big mistake. He just smiled and shook his head saying, "Not my call" and pointed back at the Imam who looked at me with that, "C'mon man" look. I pushed on.

While the disparate treatment meted out by the Black car's Imam serving the Black camper in front of me receiving two patties and the White guy, me, getting only one patty may, on its face, be resolved along racial lines, that would be a mistake. While race may be a predictor of disparate treatment among campers, I found it rarely was the sole or even dispositive rationale for such treatment.

When it came to chow, the servers had pretty much an unfettered ability to determine portion sizes and seconds. That one camper would get two burger patties from one server on Wednesday and only one chicken leg on Thursday from another server generally had more to do with the personal relationship between the server and served than with either's skin color or ethnicity. The Imam's disproportionate servings were far more likely the result of an economic relationship between the Imam and the over-served than any kind of racial profiling. Perhaps the over-served was purchasing commissary items or contraband for the Imam. No one asked. No one cared. This is how every inmate silently supported every other inmate in making their bit go faster and easier.

The unintended consequence of a reward system based on personal relationships is that, for me, it reinforced portion control at each serving. As I had no personal relationships coming into camp and, given my isolationist approach to camp survival, was not likely to build any relationships any time soon, I could depend upon the limited amount of protein served out by the BOP on a daily basis. Nothing cuts calories more efficiently than short-term, externally-enforced portion control.

And make no mistake, the BOP sense of individual protein portion was nothing like that in the free world. On burger Wednesdays, the burger is not a Big Mac; hell it's not even a quarter-pounder. It is the Junior burger – 1.6 ounces or 46 grams of beef. That is the burger that comes in the McDonald's Happy Meal. Thursday's chicken is the equivalent of a Boston Market Dark Chicken Kids Meal – a thigh and a drumstick – 1.16 ounces or 33 grams of protein. Chicken Patty Tuesday or Fish Friday are no more generous in serving size.

This enforced portion control did not mean, however, that that the campers went hungry. As I have said, it is just as easy to gain weight in a federal prison as it is to lose the pounds. As restrictive as the BOP is in its protein allotments, it is wholly unrestricted when it comes to the individual portion of carbs doled out at each meal. When it came to carb servings, particularly at lunch, the BOP wasn't just laissez faire, it was laissez les bon temps roullez.

Picture if you will a compartmentalized TV dinner or, better yet, a Swanson Hungry Man Dinner container – say the Salisbury steak. Now increase the tray size by about 1/4 where the largest area – the entree portion – sits in the middle with two rectangular portions on either side, one rectangular portion above the entree and two circles for desserts at the upper right and left corners. Now you have the standard issue BOP dining tray used for all meals at all times (except when the sewage pipe overflows in the kitchen and maintenance has to cut off the water line to repair it meaning that there is no tray washing capacity thereby requiring the use of disposal Styrofoam trays…or we're in the time of a pandemic…but I digress).

Unlike your Swanson Hungry Man version, the BOP does not put the entree (which at lunch is the stand-alone protein) in the entree compartment of the parallelogram; the protein was wedged into the one of the side rectangle compartments. This is to save the largest area on a BOP tray which is reserved for, with few exceptions, the starches: mashed potatoes, French fries or white rice. And the serving sizes would be enough to feed a family of four – the French fry equivalent of four small McDonald's fries per serving. In the other rectangular compartment on either side of and above the potatoes sat the complex carbs: beans of all type (lima, red, black, kidney – you name the bean we had it) and carbo veggies – primarily canned peas, carrots, and corn.

The circular components were for soups (generally adding water and stock to old veggies) and desserts which I will go into at greater length later on when I recount my time as the Baker of Fairton.

Chapter 15
Dinner: Food Fight –
the Battle for Protein

Dinner was a food fight between me and the protein served on the line. This was because, at dinner, the protein served was either (1) inedible; (2) not extractable from the starch it was prepared with; or (3) extractable with benefits. The inedible for me was the beef taco meat which presented itself in an orange-toned grease running through the crumbled beef. In March 2020, Reuters reported that "[t]he U.S. Bureau of Prisons lacks policies to safeguard against serving potentially contaminated food to its inmates, a problem that led it to buy substandard products, including whole cow hearts disguised as ground beef, the Justice Department's internal watchdog has found." As the only time I had seen cow organs in food packaging was when they were prepared and served to Addie – a buddy's dog – I took a pass on beef taco night and all other dinners that used crumbled ground "beef."

The non-extractable meals were the pastas with meat sauce in which no amount of effort could separate the carb from the protein. I stayed away from the soups with meat or chicken in them but did take those with fish or fake crab.

The far more common dinner experience was the extractable with benefits; those meals where the shrimp (yes, we had baby shrimp though I did not see this until the very end of 2019 and into 2020; shrimp made it on the menu on five of my dinner logs) or chicken fried rice, pork lo mein, Swedish meatballs, and the chef salad.

The key to extractable with benefits was the benefits – items purchased at the commissary that allowed me to take the extracted protein and make a meal out of it. The primary benefit added to protein was mayonnaise which turned any extracted dinner protein into a meal – think chicken salad, turkey salad, beef salad, pork salad. I had two jars of mayonnaise in my locker at all times.

As mayo was a critical component of my diet, I would be remiss to pass over it without a couple thoughts on this miracle (though not Miracle Whip) product. Two things I learned about mayonnaise on the inside: 1. It does not have to be refrigerated (at least not the kind we purchased at commissary); my jars lasted one to two weeks in my locker with no taste degradation or evident spoilage. 2. The best way to get every drop of mayo out of the jar is a technique called "helicoptering" showed to me by my bunky P2 who wrapped a long shoelace around the neck of the sealed jar and proceeded to whip the jar around in circles in front of him like the rotor blade of a helicopter forcing all the mayo inside to pack up to the lid of the jar. Who says the BOP doesn't teach you life skills on the inside? Finally, I never measured out the mayo I used to doctor up any of my dinners; I laid it on as thick as necessary to make the protein go down. To me, the caloric load of the mayo was worth it as it provided me a palatable way to consume the dinner protein and kept me full enough for the carbo-palooza.

Dinners which were inedible or non-extractable required a full substitution which became more frequent as I got further into my sentence. There were only two full dinner substitutes that made it for me:

Mack-and-Mayo. Coming into camp, I figured that tuna fish would be a staple of my diet if I could not make the food on the chow line work. I was surprised to find that the Chicken of the Sea tuna fish I purchased at the commissary to be lacking in taste regardless of the amount of mayonnaise I slathered on it (I never skimped on mayo). I found myself doing the unheard of at the camp – eating my commissary-purchased mackerel. Three-ounce pouches of this oily fish were considered currency at Fairton as they were $.95/pouch at commissary which set the monetary exchange rate: three macks to get your laundry washed, dried, and folded; four macks for a haircut; two macks for a single serve apple pie swiped from the kitchen. Eating a pouch of mackerel was the equivalent of pulling out your wallet in the free world and eating one of its dollar bills (Note: because mackerel pouches were used as currency, I had to purchase fresh pouches each week rather than use macks that were in circulation for months as the passing of pouches degraded the mackerel over time into fish mush rather than chunks. This made my consumed mackerel a more expensive proposition as the mack exchange rate in the camp was 3 for 2–60 mack pouches for $40.00. During football season, I kept a running mack account with the house at this exchange rate but never used house macks for consumption).

Mackerel by the numbers:
Product of Thailand packaged under the name "Fresh Catch"
Unite size: 3.53 ounces.
Calories: 110 per serving (1 serving per pouch)
Carbs: 0
Fat: 4.5 grams
Sodium: 320 mg

Minced Baby Clams. This was a surprise for me; a pouch of cleaned and cooked minced baby clams packed in oil. As a dinner substitute, I would take a few bites of the rice or noodle dish served on chow line, add the baby clams, throw some hot chili oil into the mix and dinner was served. The hot chili oil was a concoction whipped up by Chino in food service when he prepared his fried rice dishes – dinner fare that was as good or better than any fried rice I had ordered in the free world.

Baby Clams by the numbers:
Product of China packaged under the label "Chicken of the Sea"
Unite size: 3.53 ounces
Calories: 150 per serving (1 serving per pouch)
Carbs: 5 grams
Fat: 9.6 grams
Sodium: 3 grams

Finally, a note about salad and vegetables in the BOP:
Salad was a planned part (on the menu sheet) of at least three dinners per week. The salad was typically of three kinds: (1) the shredded salad in which all the vegetables (primarily carrots, cucumbers, onions) were put through a shredding slicer; (2) chopped salad in which food service would use a knife to cut lettuce, cucumbers and tomatoes; and (3) cole slaw – a mayonnaise-based cabbage concoction sweetened with sugar. The dressings were either pre-packaged low-fat French or Ranch or kitchen-made honey mustard with the

emphasis on honey. The chopped salad was a high valued commodity as it presented the only fresh vegetables opportunity in the BOP; the shredded salad tended to get watered down and, therefore, not as high value as it did not keep.

Beyond the chopped and shredded salads, there were no fresh vegetables served on the chow line. In the beginning, I took the canned vegetables onto my tray, figuring that eating them would be important for my diet. I soon began to pick at them as they were primarily corn, carrots and peas (more starch than veggie) and the kitchen added sugar to much of them. After a few months, I declined vegetables altogether. This despite my mother's admonition that "even canned vegetables have nutrients."

Going cold turkey on vegetables should be undertaken at your own risk. As I have said, the major noticeable impact is not in the kitchen but in the bathroom. In the free world, if you have access to fresh vegetables, by all means substitute them in for any snacks and add them to any meal. I did not notice any stalling out of my diet on the rare days that I loaded up on fresh vegetables.

The other consequence of going cold turkey on veggies was a curious change in my appetite – one I had never experienced: I started to crave fresh carrots. I only saw raw carrots and celery sticks served on the chow line twice in the Jailbird Diet days I spent at Fairton – both times, I ran to my locker, retrieved my large bowl, and went back to grab as many as I could.

When I came into camp, I immediately started thinking about what meal I would have on the day I packed out. I even asked others as they approached their pack out dates what they would have: Harry – a black-and-white milk shake; Bob Lee – his wife's pot roast; Big Ben – a McDonald's happy meal (he had a 4-year-old daughter); Norad – seafood, any seafood. I figured mine would be like the meal I had going in – a lobster roll.

As the day for my release approached, Shelly asked me what I wanted her to bring for me to eat in the car on the ride back to Philly. I told her fresh carrot sticks. And that is what I had: fresh carrot sticks to dip in Sabra-brand hummus with red peppers. As I write this, I am now 30 days out of prison, and not a day has gone by that I have not eaten a handful of carrot sticks with salt; A curious turn for my eating habits as the last time carrot sticks were part of my diet was in the 1960s when my mom would pack them for our family weekend road trips to the Jersey Shore.

Chapter 16
Snack Attack

I have mentioned commissary as an integral part of protein and an enhancement to my in-meal diet. It was equally important to my diet supplements which had an impact on my diet that cannot be overstated and, without which, my attempt at 100 pounds would have been far more precarious and far more Draconian.

So allow me first a few words on commissary.

Commissary exists at all BOP facilities; its workings and inventory varying from place to place (or so I am told). Here's how it worked at Fairton. Every Saturday, the camper-manager of commissary would place a commissary print-out listing all items for sale on each camper's bed. Each camper, if they had money wired into their commissary account, could spend a maximum of $360.00 per month on these items (the max was raised during the holiday season – November and December – to $500.00 per month). On Sunday, each camper would place his completed commissary sheet into an empty laundry bag with his name on it and place that bag into a duffle bag hanging at the cop station. The following Thursday, campers would get a ride or walk up the road to the commissary warehouse to pick up their goodies.

I looked forward to Commissary Thursday as it marked the only time I could walk down a road other than moving counter clockwise around the track surrounding Central Park. Up and back was my favorite 1.2 miles walked each week.

The list of commissary food items was, to my mind, extensive. The groupings ranged from snacks (potato chips, pretzels, trail mix etc.) to candies (Snicker, M&Ms, Jolly Ranchers, Lemon Drops, Hershey with Almonds etc.) to condiments (think the greatest hits from a McCormack spice rack) to sauces (hot-and-sour, barbecue, mayonnaise etc.) to jarred veggies (jalapeño, and spicy peppers) to proteins (pouches of mackerel, tuna fish, minced baby clams) to whole meals (Kosher chicken dinner). The selection would put any bodega to shame.

During the Christmas season the BOP, in a fit of holiday cheer, would put some high-demand junk food into the mix, most notably the quart-size container of Fluff marshmallow and a salty-spicy assault on your tastebuds called Whole Shebang chips. On Christmas Day, the BOP would hand each camper a bag of goodies – the underground economy valued the entire contents of a bag at 18 mackerel.

Crap Game ran the commissary. While not a shot caller of the White Car, he carried a lot of weight at the camp as he was the access point for the most high valued commodities in the camp – sneakers. While a good number of the Black and Spanish cars got their sneakers through a footsie exchange at visits (I assure you Left did not purchase his LeBron Witness II's through the commissary), most guys did get their sneakers through Crap Game. And because sneakers were not carried in the regular inventory, Crap Game could set aside the highest value sneakers for the highest valued campers. Crap Game ate better than any camper I knew, always seeming to have access to fresh fruits and vegetables, scoffing at those slumming it through the chicken fried rice Sundays or Taco Mondays; his clothes were tailored by Le Carre. In short, Crap Game had figured out how to work the system from his commissary perch better than any camper in the joint. And he was doing it with less than a three-year bit.

What commissary provided me outside of my meals was like what happens in Vegas – it never happens. While my logs somewhat scrupulously recorded my food intake across three meals each day, they did not record my snacking between meals and yes, I snacked between meals.

I packed two food products in my locker for snacking from the first week I surrendered until the day I packed out ten months later: peanut butter and cheese.

First allow me an opportunity to thank the hard-working men and women at the Hometown Peanut Butter Factory in Sparks Nevada. Without your jars of crunchy peanut butter I would not be 2/3s of the man I was when I walked into prison.

Peanut Butter by the numbers:

Product of USA packaged under the label "Hometown"

Unite size: 2 tablespoons

Calories: 190 per serving (16 serving per 510-ounce jar)

Carbs: 6 grams

Fat: 15 grams

Sodium: 125 mg

As I did not have a tablespoon to measure servings, I averaged my serving size over number of days it took me to consume an entire jar; as this usually took between 12 and 14 days, I calculated my daily consumption of peanut butter to be over 200 calories. Given my total calorie intake over three meals to be roughly 1,500 to 1,800 per day (just a guess), peanut butter added 20% to my daily calorie intake or 15% of my total calories per day.

Though I had not consumed peanut butter ever on such a regular basis ever in my life, I did come by my love of peanut butter honestly and for that I can thank my mother.

Connie Smukler was a health food nut decades before health food became a thing – I am talking the 1960s. When Vitamin C became hot, we ate oranges; protein the rage, we ate liver; flax seed the elixir du jour, it was baking in the oven and hidden (as though you could hide flax seed anywhere) in our oatmeal. We were the only house in post-card suburbia to hand out mini SunMaid raisin boxes for Halloween! Nature's candy never beat a Milky War bar in my eyes but my mom was not going to be the one to corrupt the neighborhood kids' diet with processed sugar products.

And Connie Smukler loved her peanut butter. Oh not the JIF, Peter Pan or Skippy variety. No, we had the health food store version – the one which, upon screwing off the top, you are confronted with a layer of oil to be stirred into the underlying peanut paste into what, ultimately, was a dryer, sandier, non-sugary version of its more mainstream brethren. Each night, my mom would take a spoonful right out of the jar; now some 50 years later I was doing the same – and doing it religiously. I don't recall a day going by that I didn't hit my jar of Hometown.

When Commissary was shut down for a week for inventory audit, the next week I signed in for two jars so as to never be without. When the jar got low, I would take my spork and dig the last vestiges of peanut butter out of the curves and ridges of the jar to extend its shelf life thereby stretching the days to meet the 200 calorie/day limit I had set for myself.

Oh and don't think, you hard working men and women of Sparks Nevada, that your jars hit the trash heap once I picked them clean. No. Nothing goes to waste in the BOP – the emptied jars were repurposed to candy holders and drinking containers; just wedge newspaper, dishwashing liquid, and some 192-degree water into the jar, screw the cap on tightly and shake vigorously for 60 seconds and you are good to go.

While I had not planned on peanut butter playing such a large role in my prison diet, I fully expected that cheese would as this dairy product was a big part of my diet (or lack thereof I should say) in the free world.

My love affair with cheese I came by honestly as well. Connie Smukler was a big fan of throwing a couple of the mini rounds of white cheese with red waxed skin packaged under the Baybel label into the grade school lunch box along with the veggies – no single serve potato chip bags for her kids!

But fast forward 50 years to prison and my first move into cheese as a dietary supplement was a failure. The gooey Gouda spread was not to my taste and was quickly 86'd from my commissary list. My second move on the cheese front – a mozzarella block – was much more to my liking though as the packaging will tell you it is not really mozzarella at all; rather a block of cheddar cheese formed, colored, and flavored to simulate mozzarella. It came three servings to a package block and, per serving, packed 100 calories, 86 grams of fat, and less than 1 gram of carbs. This was my go-to dairy snack for months until I fell for my true love – government cheese.

As you would expect, government cheese was a white, American style cheese a bit dryer and less plasticky tasting than a Kraft American single. I discovered this cheese when I was putting together dinner bags for New Year's Day (see Chapter 21, Do The Hustle). This cheese comes in pre-sliced two-foot blocks and was not available through the commissary. While I call it government cheese which it technically was, the blocks came with Chinese writing on the sides, so to this day I don't really know what it was. Furthering the mystery was a strange property it had unlike any American slice I had encountered in the free world: if you wanted to eat a slice in pieces, no matter which side you attempted to divide, it would tear down a perfectly straight line. As I write this, I am beginning to wonder if this was really cheese at all. Oh well, just water (and maybe cows' milk I hope) under the bridge at this point.

While peanut butter was primarily a night time snack, cheese was my snack of choice throughout the day; I would nibble through two or three pieces a day, generally in the breaks between walking. Sometimes I would use cheese as part of my dinner substitutes; melt three pieces of cheese in my commissary bowl then scoop mack and mayo or minced clams on top.

My third snack food grouping was chocolate. So I'm going to say it flat out and without qualification – no diet, whether this or any other, should go without chocolate. In my world, life is too short to go a day without chocolate. There I said it.

Not one day went by at Camp Fairton that I did not pop one, two, three, ok at times four peanut M&Ms into my mouth. It started with one after lunch then one after dinner. Then it moved to two after lunch and dinner and one or two before bed. My daily processed sugar count was so low that I looked forward to my candy fix each day – perfecting a technique of chewing the M&Ms at the front of my teeth and tip of my tongue to extract the greatest chocolate sensation possible. These chocolate bursts were the oases in my food desert. So much so that they began to play with my mind: I developed a theory of M&M color differentiation such that the typically smaller brown M&Ms were more likely to have a darker chocolate taste than their red, yellow, blue and green sisters. Now that I am in the free world, it seems that I am not alone. In the movie, *The Wedding Planner,* there is this scene between the wedding planner, Mary (Jennifer Lopez) and Steve (Mathew McConaughey):

Mary: What are you doing?

Steve: [eating M&Ms] I only eat the brown ones.

Mary: Because?

Steve: Well, because I figure they have less artificial coloring because chocolate is already brown.

Mary: That's very scientific of you Dr. Steve.

I knew it…I just knew it!

Toward the end of my camp stay, I diversified my candy selection. That is, if you consider sugar free butterscotch suckers to be candy. Which you should if you compare the per piece calories to peanut M&Ms: The M&Ms come 25 pieces to a pack and a pack totals 250 calories or 10 calories per piece; the commissary's sugar free butterscotch suckers – Gracey's Goodies – packs 50 calories into a three-piece serving or 16.6 calories per piece. How a candy labeled sugar free delivers more calories than a peanut M&M is a mystery to me.

But I'm not hating on Gracey or her goodies as I quickly became addicted to her butterscotch. I limited myself to three per day and only after we were cleared for outside after the 4:00 P.M. count which was usually around 5:00 P.M. My schedule toward the end had an hour blocked out for walking from 5:00 P.M. to 6:00 P.M. This gave me time to get two miles in before my one hour of television a day between 6:00 P.M. and 7:00 P.M. (30 minutes of local then 30 minutes of national news). I would carry my three Gracey's Goodies in my pocket and pop one before each mile I began. Two before 6:00 P.M. and one for my last laps at 7:00 P.M.

I added one more snack to the repertoire around this same time period – a few pinches of instant oatmeal; not just any oatmeal but the maple oatmeal processed by the senors and senoritas at the Granvita packaging plant in Mexico. These single serving packs were designed to be mixed with 192-degree water then served with milk. I ate the powdery oats right out of the packet – a crazy good mix of maple-flavored sugar, salt, and oats. But as all snacks, it did not come without a price. A 1.23-ounce single serving packet came with 140 calories and 27.6 grams of carbohydrates – not a snack to be taken in anything but small quantities. My oatmeal consuming rule was as follows: a packet had to last four days and, therefore, was to be consumed at a rate of three pinches every count time (two counts per day on weekdays; three counts per day on weekends). This meant I would max out my oatmeal calorie count per day at 35.

As you can tell, I believe the sugar provided in small doses on a daily basis was a critical component of my diet. But the Jailbird Diet takeaway is to introduce sugar under strict conditions:

First, don't park your sugar consumption inside a meal – my lunches and dinners held very little sugar in any of them. I rarely touched a sweet side dish and stayed away from the soups, salads (particularly the kitchen-made dressings) and the cole slaw as much as possible. I stayed away from baked desserts taking only the occasional Pierre's ice cream.

Second, take your sugar in small increments as that is all you will need to curb your sugar craving (and you will crave sugar, though I found my sugar craving ran more to natural fruit sugar than to processed candies). Small bite size candies work best.

Third, and perhaps most important, create consumption rules for your sugar. My M&Ms came only in ones or twos immediately after my lunch and dinner meals. My Gracey Goodies only came at the beginning of my last three miles of the day after the 5:00 PM clear for outside. My pinches of instant oatmeal only came during count time.

If you follow these rules for your sugar snacking, you will get enough processed sugar to keep your body satisfied and won't blow up your calorie count to piss off Lady Detecto the next morning.

Setting boundaries for your food choices is the main takeaway across all of my food choices – not just sweet snacking.

I did not place potatoes, rice, beans or any of the starches on my Swanson Hungry Man tray. Lunch and dinner became nothing more than fueling stations for protein. When the protein were inedible for me as stand alone, I added fat in the form of mayonnaise. Breakfast was a fueling station for bran and calcium; snacks for adding protein (peanut butter and cheeses) and sugars to the fuel mix.

I do not know if the if the sequencing of my fuels – bran/calcium in the morning; protein in the late morning and early afternoon, and sugars in the evening triggered some bio-chemical reaction that allowed for consistent sustained weight loss over my Jailbird Diet days. I do know that the sequencing gave me the strength and stamina to walk upward of five hours per day and weight train in the sixth hour.

One last word on food.

As you can tell, my diet was almost entirely devoid of fresh vegetables – a choice made for me by the BOP. It also presented limited opportunities for fresh fruit as the mainstay of our fruit diet were apples and pears which often-times were inedible. It was also not a good idea to store any quantities of fruit in your locker for snacking between meals as this was considered contraband by the cops.

I assume that, had I access to fresh veggies and fruit, my craving for processed sugar may have been slaked by carrots rather than butterscotch; oranges rather than oatmeal. I am equally confident that introduction of natural sugars at the expense of processed sugars would have led to a more healthy diet. What I don't know is whether introduction of these natural sugars would have made my weight loss more difficult to achieve. Open access to raw fruits and vegetables is also open access to calories; and these are calories far more easily rationalized in large quantities into your diet than M&Ms and suckers.

The rule I would use in the free world to recognize the swapping out of natural for processed sugar is to maintain the caloric proportions and the scheduling regimens I established in prison. Treat your fresh fruits and raw vegetables as I treated my sugary snacks: set defined caloric limits for them and consume them at defined times outside of your meal times. A 7" long carrot is 30 calories – 5 more than a peanut M&M; a small orange is 45 calories – 5 less than two peanut M&Ms; a medium sized apple has 95 calories and 25 grams of carbs – the equivalent of my daily consumption of four peanut M&Ms.

In total, my daily non-meal sugar consumption approached 250–400 calories. My daily in-meal calorie consumption was 1500 to 1800 calories; nearly 20% of my calories coming from non-meal-based sugars. Setting this kind of limit on your non-meal raw vegetables and fresh fruit and also setting schedule limits (before your walks, after your meals etc.) will allow you to swap good sugars for bad and not blow up your diet. Apply the adage "good fences make good neighbors" to your diet – good boundaries make good calories. It was only when these fences began to break down that I hit the weight loss wall. That time, which you will read about in a later chapter, when I became the Baker of Fairton.

Part III
Chasing 100

Chapter 17
Lady D

Day 1. June 18, 2019
285: 100 Pounds to Go

"When we consider what, to use the words of the catechism, is the chief end of man, and what are true necessities and means of life, it appears as if men had deliberately chosen the common mode of living because they preferred it to any other. Yet they honestly think there is no choice left. But alert and healthy natures remember that the sun rose clear. It is never too late to give up our prejudices. No way of thinking or doing, however ancient, can be trusted without proof."

Thoreau, Walden, p. 6

She stands statuesque like a marble goddess. Rigid, straight. Eye forward. Never wavering. Never wilting. An anomaly of shape and tone in a world of men bent and broken. She stands in a dimly lit hallway of poured concrete floor and cinderblock walls. Standing just outside the open doorway of the bathroom – as though telling all who enter and leave – those who preen before the mirrors, suck in their guts, pump out their chests – not to be fooled – mirrors are just illusions, she is the truth.

I go to bed each night thinking of our moment the next morning together. For there she stood in the hallway the first morning that I rose at camp – erect against the white cinderblock – the one beacon of truth and constancy that this place affords to those who have come here seeking nothing more that the swift movement of the earth around the sun.

I have looked into her eyes each morning from the first day I arrived. She has the tattoo of a red cardinal above her right cheek. With us it is always the same dance.

I approach directly and stand before her. I am wearing gym shorts, a T-shirt, and my shower shoes. I am taller than she, made even taller when I stand on her feet. I look down at her and take her chin between my thumb and forefinger. I move it to the right as though inspecting her profile…100…further…150…further…200…further…250…stop.

Now I take a strand of her hair and fling it to the right across her brow; an act of disgust? despair? The wisp moves across her face as if in flight. She closes her eye as the strand moves above it and off her face as if disappointed with my rudeness. But I know my movements mean nothing to her. She has seen the anger, hope, misery of men like me every day she has stood here. She doesn't judge as she judges. At 50 it stops…it can go no further.

She refuses to look me in the eye and tell me the truth. But what am I here for if not to gain approval in her eye? If not to gain by losing?

Now I gently take this same strand – now timid? hopeful? afraid? – and move it haltingly back to the left across her brow not knowing when I have gone too far. Never knowing that precise moment when it is too late – when she tells me I must stop…tells me that she is ready to open her eye and reveal the truth; the truth about me that only she knows and only she can reveal.

50…further left…45…further left…40…further left…at 37 her eye starts to flutter ever so haltingly…a little girl waking up from a deep sleep clinging to the last images of a dream. At 35 she is wide awake…her eye wide open staring directly back at me – 285.

One of her sisters was waiting in the chow hall (the other we met when our story began) against the western wall wedged between the stackable plastic chairs and table with the microwave. Placed in an ironic setting (a Detecto in a chow hall – as disturbing as one placed by the counter of a Dunkin' Donuts!). And she with the lazy eye requiring the turning of her head to get her to respond; like the banging of an adolescent on a pinball machine to free the stuck flipper.

And why two in the same building? I stay true to my first love waiting in the hallway visiting her sister only for validation; never to set the mark, simply to confirm it. I never once cheat on her. I could have. Standing, or stooping I should say, right next to her in the hallway is the Health-O-Meter Pro Series Large Raised Dial Platform – a needle bouncing clockwise around a dial landing on a hash mark sitting between two numbers. (120 men and three scales to choose from. Really?) But the Health-O-Meter is just a pale imitation in form and design. And so fickle...so easily manipulated. I didn't even approach it for to do so would be cheating myself...cheating us.

That is where our affair began. Every morning. After I set down my cereal, my bowl, my MP3 and headset, and my spoon at my table in the chow hall; how much could a spoon weigh? It didn't matter. After I took one more shot at the urinal (how much could the water weigh? It didn't matter). At a time when I was most vulnerable, she was there – stoic, graceful, unwavering – the one beacon I could set my days and nights by all my days at Fairton.

The journey would begin and end with her.

Spurred on by Lady D each morning and the utter frustration I would feel when my morning weigh in did not show progress, I watched everything that went into my mouth at every meal, every day. When you are recording number of bites of pastry or starch after each meal, your level of vigilance will pay off in the long run. But the necessary prerequisite for such vigilance is weighing yourself every morning: that feeling of frustration and angst in failing should the weigh show progress has stalled; that feeling of self-satisfaction when the weight moves, ever so slightly more to the left than it did the day before; these feelings define the Jailbird Diet.

Achieving this mindset for me was not difficult: if I failed at the one goal I had told my family and friends I would achieve in prison, then the experience itself would be a net loss for me. If however I succeeded, the entire crazy, dehumanizing, at times ridiculous experience that is prison would, on some level, have all been worth it. Of all things that made significant weight loss a reality for me, the fact that the success or failure of my entire prison experience rested on such weight loss, may have been the greatest predictor of success.

Perhaps the fundamental takeaway for those undertaking this journey outside of prison is this: If the entire success or failure of each day rests upon Lady D the following morning, you will keep moving and keep monitoring your food with a vigilance that allows for little deviation from the program. If something else in your mind separates your good days from bad days, you probably will not push yourself to move and monitor and will not sustain short-term weight loss. Move. Monitor. Lose Weight. Move. Monitor. Lose Weight. Period.

That is why the Jailbird Diet is not for the faint of heart. Something inside of you must propel you to move, isolate, simplify; to change the way you live and, more importantly, what you process on a daily basis; something inside you must want weight loss more than anything you want that day. No diet can give that to you. That is what you must bring to the diet.

But if you bring that desire to the diet, you will understand what I am about to tell you:

There can be no journey without the eye of the truth staring back at you each morning. She will be the last one you think of as you place your head on the pillow at night. There will be days you wake up like a child on Christmas morning running to tear open the gift wrap at the base of the tree; and days that you will drag your feet in her presence knowing that her truth is not the news you want to start off your day. But whether she fulfills your expectations or meets your disappointment, you will always go back to her. You will pat yourself on the back for job well done or leave her in frustration – asking yourself what could I have done to make her see me differently – see me as less than I am and therefore greater than I was yesterday. But she will always be there – inviolate, dispassionate, honest. She will define me each morning every day of my journey…every step of my journey.

285.

The first step.

Chapter 18
Professor Mead and Wilson

Day 7. June 25, 2019

281: 96 Pounds to Go

Professor Mead

A balance beam (or other reliable) scale you can depend on begins the journey each day. But there is no journey if it is not memorialized. Every day.

In 1988, I went out to Wisconsin to work on Herb Kohl's maiden run for the U.S. Senate. Herb had grown up bagging groceries for his dad, Max Kohl, in his grocery market in Milwaukee; a market that would grow in the 1940s into a supermarket chain in Southeastern Wisconsin known as Kohl's Food Stores then into the largest supermarket chain across Wisconsin in the 1960s and ultimately Kohl's Department Stores which went onto become one of the largest department store chains in the country.

In the summer of 1988, I was the Kohl campaign's statewide field director overseeing field offices in Green Bay, Eau Claire, Stevens Points, LaCrosse, Madison, and Milwaukee. Each day, we would send field staffers and volunteers door-to-door to canvass prospective voters. They key to this field program, and any other worth engaging in, is data. I would tell the field directors in each office that a canvasser who comes back without data is not a canvasser, he or she is just a kid taking a walk.

The other message I would deliver to the field was this: data is not good or bad because of the story it tells; it is good because it is accurate and bad because it is inaccurate; and accuracy is a function of the contemporaneous recording of events. Field organizers without clipboards and a pen (this was the 1980s) are not field organizers, they are a waste of time and resources.

I began my journey at Fairton with Professor Mead – a 1 Subject, Wide Ruled, Wireless "Neatbook" Notebook, 10 1/2 in × 8 in, 80 sheets – an organizer I received from a camper my very first night at camp on June 17, 2019. On the cover, the "professor" boldly states his motto: Learn. Organize. Create.

While my first recorded entry was my second day in prison, 6.19, my first recorded weight was on Day 7, June 25th–28th. My last recorded entry was the morning of April 29, 2020 – the day I left Fairton for good – 185. I recorded my journey every day of my prison stay. I carried my notebook and pen to my outdoor office in the park and kept them with my stack of books under my bed in the housing unit.

The data points were recorded after breakfast, lunch and dinner: the day and date; weight taken between 6:00 A.M. and 6:30 A.M. each morning; breakfast, lunch and dinner scribbled under the headers B, L, and D with the major components of each meal listed below. Vertically down the page, I recorded the laps and miles walked with the times of completion. When I began my work in the weight room, I recorded the time of session and the muscle group we worked on.

There were some data points I probably should have recorded but did not. With few exceptions, I rarely recorded my after-meal snacks or the cheating I did when I became the Baker of Fairton (see Part VIII. Chapter 2). At first, the snacking was so minimal – one peanut M&M after lunch and one after dinner – that I did not think recording the event was necessary.

My expansion of these snacks in the last couple months to include sugar-free butterscotch suckers and pinches of maple walnut oatmeal packs should have been noted in my daily log as they were contributing a more significant share to my daily calorie count. Don't make this mistake – record everything and let the potato chips fall where they may.

In my first recorded log entry the page is entirely filled with political tidbits taken from the news:

"Poll shows Biden up 9, Sanders up, Warren up."

I had not yet moved to record my laps or meals in daily log form. My political scribbles continued on 6.19 noting "Warren passing Sanders in a Nevada poll, Donald Trump Jr.'s Trump Tower statement, Hope Hicks moving back to Trump White House from Fox News, and Sara Huckabee Sanders running for Senate in Arkansas." The June 19th log did mark the first memorialization of walking; "9:48 M1." On 6.21, I am off politics altogether and for the next six weeks, my logs reflected a personal working through of the intellectual foundation for my diet – thoughts, as you know by now, profoundly influenced by my reading of one book in particular, Henry David Thoreau's, "Walden."

That I shed my political skin in these logs so quickly was surprising. Since January 1987 – the month I left the practice of law to join Mayor W. Wilson Goode's re-election campaign in Philadelphia – my life beyond family and friends was devoted to politics; it was both my vocation and avocation. Some of my greatest and longest friendships were forged on and around the political battlefield. That it took only a matter of days to pivot, for the most part, away from political discourse and engagement surprises me even as I write this looking back now at the end of my journey.

I say "for the most part" because I did not toss off my political hat entirely. I was putting together rifts I would post under the tag: "Sincerely 76315-066." I composed two such blog posts for smerconish.com – a website produced by the host of the eponymous television show on CNN aired Saturday mornings and weekday talk radio show on Sirius XM (also an author, his latest, "Talk" – a great read I devoured in a day and a night at camp). Michael Smerconish is a good friend who I met in 1987 when we were working on opposite sides of a Philadelphia mayoral campaign; he for the former police commissioner and mayor Frank Rizzo, I for the incumbent mayor seeking re-election, W. Wilson Goode (That we became friends as competitors on different sides of the political spectrum speaks perhaps to the times when those in the game could see beyond the political divide to that which we have in common but that again is a book for another time and another author). Michael's other claim to fame for me is the he was the very last friend to visit me at Fairton before all visitations were shut down due to the pandemic.

I submitted two blog posts for smerconish.com while inside, both written into my logbook: one an analysis of the August Democrat presidential debate winners and losers; the other, two weeks prior to the Iowa Caucus, in which I predicted mayor Pete Buttegieg would win the Iowa Caucus and Senator Amy Klobuchar was best suited to be the Democrat nominee's Vice-Presidential pick. That was the last time I used the notebook for commentary.

But it was clear that my brain was retooling itself away from politics toward wrestling with issues of faith, religion, good, and evil and weight loss…It would only be much later that I would synthesize these concepts into a holistic approach toward dieting which forms the basis of the Jailbird Diet and much of the narrative of the chapter, "Solitude…and SCUBA."

Sunday June 23 – Day 6 of incarceration – marked the first log entry of walking miles annotated by time of day. It begins, however, with this:

"First loud altercation [I have witnessed]…in dining room. Everyone moves to see what's happening…when one bad apple really does impact everyone, all take interest.

Ex[ample]: Told to volunteer for Breathalyzer as if one fails its bad for all – because I am in Times Square, it's easier for me – take one for the team."

The next day, June 24, I recorded my first weight – 281: four pounds down from the day I entered seven days earlier. Every day for the next 310 days, I recorded weight, meals, laps, weight room, and random thoughts.

The data I collected, was useful in tweaking my diet and exercise regimens when the need arose. As you will read, my recorded plateau in January led me to reassess my baking career and throw in my apron to commit myself to reaching the 100-pound goal. Being able to see the plateau in black and white in my daily log drove the message home for me – I needed to switch up my daily routine.

But the daily log has a much greater impact on your journey particularly in the early phases when your deepest and fastest weight drop will, most likely, occur; the log is a daily affirmation that the effort you are putting into the journey is working. Turning the pages and seeing the number at the upper left-hand corner of the notebook drop each morning that I opened the notebook was a reaffirmation; when it did not drop it was a recommitment.

Every lap. On paper. Every mile. On paper. Every meal. On paper. Every meeting with Lady D. On paper. If it didn't get recorded, it didn't happen.

In 1846, Daniel Mead founded the Mead Corporation in Dayton, Ohio. The firm originally manufactured paper, but the company dramatically expanded its product line during the twentieth century. By the time of Daniel Mead's death in 1891, the Mead Corporation was one of the largest paper producers in the United States, with paper mills in Kingsport, Tennessee, Brunswick, Georgia, and Escanaba, Michigan, as well as several plants in Ohio.

Wilson

"What's your point. We might just make it? Did that thought ever cross your brain? Well regardless. I would rather take my chance out on the ocean then to stay here and die on this shit hole island spending the rest of my life talking to a goddamn volleyball."

After the first couple of weeks in prison, I began to openly refer to my plastic chair as Wilson – the name Tom Hanks's character gave for his volleyball companion in the 2000 movie classic, *Castaway*.

In many ways I identified with the Hanks character. Fairton was an island separated from family and friends – a deep woods on one side, a medium security prison on the other; a world I had only read about and was quite confident I would never have to experience. Yet here I was.

In the first days, I recall three conversations of any real length. With one exception, these were the longest conversations I would have in my ten-month stay: Scottie, my tour guide, the first evening I arrived, providing me the lay of the land both in terms of landscape and camper profiles. Crap Game who ran the commissary – the camp canteen where we could place our order for everything from underwear and sneakers to junk food, peanut butter and mackerel to hair and dental hygiene products; our conversation my first night at Fairton was Crap Game schooling me on how to fill out my first order form. Finally, Pilot who gave me a deep dive into the rules and regulations – it was Pilot who tipped me off to the phone room sneaker lost and found that led me to my LeBron Witness IIs (see Part VI, Chapter 2, "What Left Left").

Beyond these three conversations, I kept to myself. I didn't seek out conversations with anyone. I quickly found that, for me, the key to my moving through this new world with the least angst possible was to stay away from the housing unit as much as possible, place myself in a position where I could read, write, puzzle, and walk, and do so with a minimum of interference from the camp and its campers; wholly unchartered territory for me as I was anything but a loner in the free world.

This was not as easy as you might think.

Outside space was as territorial as seating arrangements in the chow hall and arranged along similar racial lines. The Black car took over the basketball court and the raised concrete pad that formed a walkway between the northside of the court and the trailer that housed the chapel, common room, and laundry.

The wooden deck of the back or westside of the housing unit was not segregated on race lines but on sports lines: it was dominated by a ping pong table where Doc would defend his championship belt against all takers – Black, White, Spanish, Asian or Indian/Pakistani; the benches on the deck taken by ping pong spectators or Doc's next victims.

This left the park area to the south of the housing unit: a wooded picnic-like area surrounded by an oval dirt track with a bocce court running away from the housing unit down the middle. The White car's table, which some in the Black car referred to as the KKK table, sat at the entrance to the bocce court. As I looked out that first morning onto the park area, I realized three things: (1) the White table would always be crowded and full of conversations neither of which suited my newly found isolationism; (2) bocce was not a game I had ever played nor cared to learn; and (3) there was no outdoor seating that looked more comfortable to sit in for sustainable periods of time than the armless stackable chair provided each camper at the foot of his bunk; the outdoor picnic table seating being pre-fabricated 14-gauge steel framed with a thermoplastic powder coat finish and no seat backs.

The solution became simple: find a table not historically claimed by any car, take my stackable armless chair to that table along with my books, puzzles, notebook, pen, MP3 player and headset, and just create my own space. It seemed curious to me that no other camper had felt the occasion to take their chair outside the housing unit or chow hall but I saw no reason why such a move would be prohibited by the BOP or frowned upon by the campers.

[Note. In the ten months I was at Fairton, I only saw one other camper bring his chair to the park and set it up by a table in the woods as I had; and that was eight months into my bit. He was the orthodox rabbi who took his chair to the table on the eastern side of the track where he would read and pray.]

The White campers were always at the White table in front of the bocce court, the Black campers hit the rabbi's table (before the rabbi got there); the Islanders would camp out in the closest table to the deck; and there was a table at the far southernmost end of the track that was rarely used (but for times when a camper, we'll call BB, would seemingly meditate there after visits on Saturday and Sunday) but that was a schlep too far.

There was a table situated between the Islander and White tables to the western edge of the track that was nobody's. On Day One, June 18, 2019, I took my armless stackable to it and planted it there the entire day. I placed my work materials on the table and quickly learned one of the most important lessons of my prison life: if you treat a physical place that has yet to be declared the space of another as your own, and continue to treat it as such by regularly establishing your presence in that space, the campers will treat it as yours and not violate the space without asking your permission.

My chair at the table declared my "ownership" of the space. My reading and writing materials on the table confirmed this "ownership." Campers knew I was working and understood that I chose to do so alone; they respected this before they even knew who I was or what I was like. On the rare occasion that a camper would come into this space, he would ask me if I minded his sitting at the table. I found this deference at first a bit disconcerting – this was a group that paid little deference to anything that was not wearing a BOP uniform. But then I came to realize that this is yet another way that campers ensure that everyone moves toward the end of their sentences without a hitch. Space that is not declared, once declared by a camper, is understood to be that camper's space only to be ceded by that camper through declaration or disuse. As long as I kept placing my chair at that particular table, leaving it to walk, eat meals, or use the bathroom but always returning to it, the table would be considered mine.

And that is how my chair became Wilson. He came out with me first thing every morning and stayed with me the entire day. When recalled from the outside for count at 4:00 P.M., Wilson and I would go to my bunk and wait for the count; when cleared back outside, Wilson and I would go back to "my" table; at 8:30 recall we would go to his designated space in the chow hall to watch TV; when recalled to the bunk for the 10:00 P.M. count, Wilson and I would go to bunk to wait for the count. After 11:00 P.M. lights out to be propped up on my bunky's chair for my nightly ascent to and morning descent from the upper berth.

Like Tom Hanks and his volley ball, Wilson and I were inseparable. He helped me establish my identity in the camp as one who needed space and was not open for long conversations; an invaluable partner in my journey as he allowed me the space and freedom to define my regimen free from camper or camp interference.

While I do not argue that one must acquire an armless plastic chair to tote around with them at all time as a necessary tool of the Jailbird Diet, I do maintain that Wilson is really the flip side of the importance of moving your body in Part 2. Shock and Awful. If at all times you are accompanied by a metaphorical Wilson you will constantly be in motion and that motion will spur on your Jailbird Diet success.

Bob Barker Industries. Injection Molded, One Piece, Intense Use Stack Chair, Constructed with high impact no break polypropylene

In the early 80s, *Bob* Barker bought a friend's small jail supply business and started supplying restaurant supplies along with personal care, bedding, clothing and security equipment to jails in North Carolina, South Carolina and Virginia. In 1986, *Bob Barker's* Company moved headquarters to downtown Fuquay Varina, North Carolina and soon after purchased a building to manufacture metal products. By the late 90s, the company had grown to over 200 employees. Contrary to prison myth, the company has no relation to the television game show host.

Chapter 19
What Left Left

Day 22. July 7, 2019

272: 87 Pounds to Go

Sunday July 7, 2019. 5:20 A.M.

Something was wrong. Just how wrong it was hard for me to tell. I had only spent one weekend at camp. Last Saturday and Sunday mornings the lights stayed off until 9:00 A.M. When you're jumping out of bed at the call of "PILL LINE" each morning at 5:45 to escape being awoken by a shower of high voltage lights, you notice when the lights stay off even a minute longer, let alone hours. Last weekend a camper told me that weekends were different; campers were allowed to sleep-in well past the weekday wake up of 6:00 A.M. And now the lights are on. Cops are yelling "COUNT" "COUNT" "STAND UP COUNT."

I jump up in the upper berth and look over to the clock on the far wall of the housing unit. It is 5:15. Guys now scrambling up out of bed trying to figure out why a count had been called four hours and 45 minuses ahead of the standard 10:30 A.M. weekend count.

From my perch in Times Square I can see through the glass windows of the double doors leading out of the unit to the bathroom and chow hall. I can see two campers, call them Left and Washington, being jacked up against the cinderblock walls of the outer hallway; two cops frisking them with an SIS officer (Special Investigations Section – the Gestapo – as I came to say: "SIS: they put the 'I' in SS) taking the lead."

Left and Washington – shot callers of the Black car – ran the gaming operation: they were the house at the black jack table, the dealers at the poker table, and ran the football betting operation giving lines on college games starting with mid-American conference games on Wednesdays (called "Maction" – think Kent State versus Miami of Ohio), NFL Thursdays, Friday and Saturday college games, then back to the NFL Sunday and Monday. Thousands of dollars wagered each weekend on football: 2-picks to 10-picks, straight lines or teasers, halftime lines and game lines, a fantasy football league, boxes and prop bets for the Super Bowl: Will San Fran QB Garoppolo attempt at least 29.5 passes? How long will the longest touchdown be – more than or less than 47.5 yards? Will Demi Lovato sing the national anthem in under 2:00 minutes? (She did – clocking in at 1:50).

But this Sunday morning in early July, football season was still a few weeks away (nobody bet baseball) so Left and Washington turned their attention to the next best money-making opportunity at the camp – jumping over the fence line to grab bags of contraband in the woods to be brought inside for sale.

As you now know, on the western edge of the camp is a thick wood that runs the entire length of the camp. Beyond the woods to the south lies Fairton-Millville Road; at times, not often, you could hear 18-wheelers running down the road; I was told the road lay about 1/4 mile through the woods. [Note: When I headed out of the camp ten months later, I asked Shelly to take me down that road; I wanted to see if the camp or its track was visible from the road; I saw nothing but thick woods – no sign of the little community on the other side of the woods or the sprawling shrine to federal incarceration that stretched out less than a mile from the road.]

That contraband was coming into the camp was no secret to campers or cops. That it was coming in through the woods, I am quite sure, was no secret to the cops either. On occasion BOP vehicles would drive down the dirt road on the wooded side of the fence line looking for contraband. Just weeks before I arrived, I was told MacDonalds cheeseburgers and fries made it into the chow hall late night; there were tales of King Crab legs and hoagies showing up.

The following is a reconstruction of the events leading up to the early count from other campers after the fact.

As the night time counts were regularly scheduled affairs – 12:30 A.M., 3:30 A.M., and 5:00 A.M. – this Sunday morning's rendezvous in the woods was scheduled between the 3:30 and 5:00 A.M. counts – time when the one night shift cop on duty is usually sitting at the desk of the

132

administrative/visiting room trailer, a few steps outside the single doorway on the Northside of the housing unit, playing on the computer. Out of sight, out of mind.

But this fine summer Sunday morning, the cop decided to take a stroll around the campsite before meeting with his back-up for the 5:00 A.M. count (counts are always conducted by two cops). This morning the cop began his rounds by heading west toward the fence line then south passed the hoops court and gym toward the track area. At some point he spots Left and Washington moving quickly – though not stealthily – from the fence line toward the door at the southwest corner of the housing unit. The chase was on. The cop radios for help. Left and Washington make it back to their beds in the White House but the cop makes them. Back up, in the form of two SIS officers arrive. Left and Washington are hauled out into the corridor where I first see them up against the wall.

Left and Washington said they were out of the unit praying (religious activity is one of the most often-used vehicles for camper misbehavior – you want to make an illegal cellphone call, go to the chapel, you want to fight, move the furniture in the chapel, got a bootleg DVD, show it in the chapel). But their boots – muddied during their sojourn into the woods – gave them away. It did not take SIS long to find the contraband dropped behind the gym – they have seen this movie before. It took less time for SIS to handcuff Left and Washington and march them off to the SHU never to be seen again at the camp.

And that was a shame.

Not because the gaming operation took a hit. As any convict or cop will tell you, the gaming operation never takes a hit (unless of course there are no games which, prior to the pandemic arriving at the camp on March 15, 2020, was unthinkable). The gaming license was quickly appropriated by two inmates each representing the Black and White cars, let's call them Russian M and Face, well in time for the start of pre-season football betting.

No, it was a shame because the mission that Left and Washington had undertaken in the woods that early Sunday morning was not a mission for hire – it was altruistic and, dare I say, patriotic. They were bringing in contraband for the Black car's Fourth of July party to be held a few days later. A greater shame in that Left was in the last three months of a seven-year bit; his tenure in the federal penitentiary system now extended as his good days would now no longer be deducted from his sentence.

At first, I asked myself why would anyone risk that much for so little? Over time, I came to realize that as much as I was in the same place experiencing the same life as others at the camp, I was really in a much different place mentally and emotionally from most of the men with whom I served time. For me, camp was just a way station – a place I would spend a relatively short amount of time until I returned to the free world. Counting your time in months is far different than counting your time in years. When you count in years, camp is not a transitionary point, it is life, death, happiness, pain, love, hate; it is not part of some life change, it is life. For Left and Washington, part of that life was crossing the fence line, receiving contraband, bringing it in, and celebrating all that you could do in this camp; it was making this camp life – their lives – the best it could be. The trade off in greater time served if caught was worth the opportunity for greater happiness in this, the one life they had.

This calculation could never make sense for me because this was not my one life – my one life was in the free world; this was like a trip to outer space with a set return date to Earth programmed into the rocket ship from the moment it launched. Campers serving less than a few years quickly come to understand the difference between those living in prison and those camping in prison. For those doing real time, months are seconds in prison. I was not one of them. I was not standing in the same shoes as Washington or Left. But in a much less metaphorical and much more real sense for what I was about to undertake, I would stand in Left's shoes.

Left's departure, though a significant loss to the Black car, was a significant gain for prisoner 76315-066.

When one of our brethren gets sent to the SHU, they go as they came in – stripped of all their worldly possessions. They leave in their greens (prison shirt and pants), and more importantly for our story, they walk out in the canvas topped and rubber-soled shoes (think poor man's boat shoes) they came in with.

And because he could only wear his boat shoes as he was cuffed and marched to the SHU, his last act at the camp was an act of love – he left his sneakers in the phone room; a signal to all the brothers he left behind that his kicks could live on at the camp even though his time had ended so abruptly.

I had come into the camp as Left had departed; walked in with greens, underwear and boat shoes. As Big Bill told me the first day, he saw me walking the track: "You gonna kill your feet in these shoes." How true how true said the sour kangaroo.

Within days of my entry I had been offered a used pair of sneakers – two sizes too small but better than boat shoes for getting around a track that was little more than tamped down dirt, gravel, embedded stones, and fallen twigs.

Day 13 and I am in the phone room for my daily 15-minute call with Shelly. And there they sat. A pair of Nike LeBron James, Witness II basketball sneakers. Not the prison commissary version of old-man Adidas or New Balance walking sneakers. The real deal kicks worn no doubt by a friend or family member who came to visit Left, clandestinely swapped behind a tree, then walked in by Left and now sitting for all to see in the phone room – fair game for anyone like me who didn't mind stepping into the shoes of another.

A camouflage design on the heel, a white rubber overlay on the toe, a mesh weave across the arch and the King James logo on both the tongue and the sole. The inmate with the least street cred in the whole damn camp now walking in the shoes of one designed by the best in the game and worn by one who had, I was told, the most street cred in the camp before meeting his ignominious end.

Each morning after my face time with Lady D, after I ate my breakfast, made my bed, and got my shower, I would strap on my King James Witness IIs and hit the trail. My LeBron's were with me every day of my journey. I walked 1,086 miles. That's 5,734,080 feet. That's 2,172,000 steps. Every one of those steps I took with King James on my feet and by my side. When the glue on the sides began to wear, I walked on. When no amount of dishwasher liquid would clean them, I walked on. When the left sole began to shred (for these soles were meant for polished wood floors and not the dirt and gravel track of Fairton), I walked on. Today they sit on a shelf – one of my most prized possessions commemorating my time at camp – an homage to the King; an homage to Left – whose slip up on that early morning of July 3rd, provided me with one of the greatest tools for my journey in its earliest days.

So treat yourself to a pair of good walking sneakers. They are a Jailbird dieter's best friend.

Nike LeBron Witness II Grey Camo Men's Basketball Shoes

The shoe is the second budget model from the LeBron Witness series. The Nike LeBron Witness II was released in October 2017 at only $100. It has the same setup as its predecessor. Starting off with the traction, it has a hexagonal diamond traction pattern that works well on both indoor and outdoor courts. The midsole has full-length Phylon and two Zoom units at the forefoot, delivering exemplary court feel. The upper is made of breathable and lightweight textile that has leather and fuse overlays for durability. This mid-top shoe comes with an inner sleeve for a better fit.

RunRepeat.com

Chapter 20
Miles to Walk Before I Sleep

Day 72. August 24, 2019

245: 60 Pounds to Go

"To walk in a winter morning in a wood where these birds abounded, their native woods, and hear the wild cockerels crow on the trees, clear and shrill for miles over the resounding earth drowning the feebler notes of other birds – think of it! It would put nations on the alert. Who would not be early to rise, and rise earlier and earlier every successive day of his life, till he became unspeakably healthy, wealthy, and wise?"
Walden p. 71

August 24, 2019 marked the first day that I was able to string five laps around the track at one walking which shows you just what kind of shape I was in when I entered Fairton. My first days I could not even make one lap without a break to deal with the pain shooting through my hip (scaling and descending their upper bunk was taking its toll). I would collapse into Wilson after each lap, prop my dead foot onto the pre-fab picnic bench I called home and took 30 minutes to read, write or crossword before getting enough energy to take the next lap.

I was the slowest camper around the track from the day I started till the day I packed out. I was not getting anything close to a cardio workout in my walking. Heck, except on the hottest of days, I did not even break a sweat. It was the constant movement that mattered, not the amount of exertion occasioned by the movement. I can say for a fact that significant short-term weight loss does not require you to burn the maximum number of calories in a workout session. At the height of my weekly weight loss I was walking three miles a day as compared to 10–12 miles a day at the end of the program when I was losing half the amount per week.

But while short-term weight loss does not require the maximum burn per workout, it does require the maximum commitment to workout. Every day. Rare Exceptions. While I was the slowest walker around the track, I was the most consistent walker of all the campers at Fairton. Beyond a few days which I bailed due to burn out, I never missed back-to-back days of walking unless I was injured (which only occurred two weeks out of the 44 I was there) and the two weeks they shut the track down at the end of my stay. Again, it was the constancy of movement brought on I believe by shock-and-awful and then routinized as part of my daily schedule that created the caloric burn necessary for short-term significant weight loss.

The idea to spend the lion share of my waking incarcerated hours moving around the track was not mine. It was Silverman's – a camper who served his time at Fairton in 2015. Over a series of pre-camp phone calls, Silverman gave me the key to surviving Fairton. His answer? Run. And run. And run some more.

That was Silverman's strategy.

Silverman averaged 15 miles a day. In my first days at camp, I was told that five laps around the track was a mile. Many months later, Pilot used a surveyor's wheel (he was the camper manager for landscaping) and found that five laps were actually short of a mile by 300 feet. From that moment on, I would tack on one lap on the path that cut diagonally across the track just to the south end of the bocce court to add the necessary 300 feet to my mile count.

At 15 miles a day, Silverman was running 75 laps primarily after work from 3:00 till 8:30 recall. Silverman also used a motivational tool – plotting the miles on a U.S. map along the route from Fairton to his summer home in Colorado.

While Silverman ran the track, few did during my stay. A camper, we'll call Jesus for his hair and beard, would run in the summer months but abruptly stopped when the temperature dropped in the Fall. The Black car had Shaun who would do sprints down the west side straightaway as part of his daily regime. The White car had S, the Spanish car, AV, but these guys were more versions of speed walking than running. Then there was AW – a self-surrendered white guy, my age, who would actually speed walk lapping me regularly around the track.

The track was only used for a foot race once during my time down. On major holidays, Jaws would set up camp competitions on the basketball court, handball court, volleyball court, and bocce court. Le Carre even built a corn hole set to regulation specs for competition. These competitions were endorsed by the BOP providing Jaws with Gatorade to distribute to the winners. On Labor Day, Jaws added a foot race to the competition schedule.

Now what happens in a federal prison when there is a prize to be awarded for a competition that no campers want to enter? Answer: A workaround. Two campers conspire to race while pre-arranging to split the winnings. So there was the Black car's entry, M – a fit 40-year-old – lining up against the White car's entry – "Murder Mike" – a 5'9" 58-year-old who came into camp 18 days before me weighing 285 pounds. M ran one lap; Murder Mike didn't make the first turn. Both split the winnings.

Another key to Silverman's strategy was taking a job down the road. For reasons I will discuss later, this was not part of my strategy. Silverman, however, was not alone in using a job down the road to do his bit. Roughly half the camp was up when lights came on at 6:00 A.M. and walking or taking the camper-provided van transport up the service road to begin the work day at 6:30. As many of the workers had access to food and microwaves up at their worksites, many cooked and ate up the road or had their lunches taken up to them leaving them away from the camp buildings the entire day.

[Aside: Campers in the federal prison system are really the last vestiges of indentured servitude in America performing tasks outside the gates of Super Max, Max, Medium, and Low facilities to which the camps are attached across the country. Campers do the jobs inmates in the higher security prisons cannot do – jobs like landscaping outside the prison fence line, driving the trash and recycling vehicles, warehousing the food, maintenance of all camp facilities etc. These jobs pay from $20.00 to $150.00 a month. The most coveted job is working for a for-profit company called UniCorp which, for the Fairton campers lucky enough to score one (there was a waiting list for them) meant primarily stripping Comcast modems before they were sent inside to the Medium to be re-built. These jobs were coveted initially for their compensation at the higher end of the wage scale then, upon passage of the First Step Act in January 2019, coveted as they were rumored to award greater time credits to reduce length of sentence (like so many rumors about the impact of the First Step Act on reducing length of sentence, none were ever confirmed).]

Silverman tracked the miles he ran on a map as though running to his home in Colorado. While I did not go to the lengths of charting the miles on a map, I would often dream as I walked that I was heading to my happy place – a spot on Sebago Lake in South Casco Maine; a picture in my mind like that painted of the lake John Fenimore Cooper called GlimmerGlass in the "Deerslayer."

"On a level with the point lay a broad sheet of water, so placid and limpid, that it resembled a bed of the pure mountain atmosphere, compressed into a setting of hills and woods. But the most striking peculiarities of this scene, were its solemn solitude and sweet repose. On all sides, wherever the eye turned, nothing met it, but the mirror-like surface of the lake, the placid void of heaven, and the dense setting of wood. In a word, the hand of man had never defaced, or deformed any part of this native scene, which lay bathed in sunlight, a glorious picture of affluent forest grandeur, softened by the balminess of June, and relieved by the beautiful variety afforded by the presence of so broad an expanse of water" (pp. 36–37).

Maintaining the dream of a place that you are walking toward, whether you actually track your progress toward that place or not, was a very real part of my walking experience – a very real part of the Jailbird Diet. I don't know whether my mind would travel to Migis Lodge while walking because Silverman put the idea of a destination in there before I ever got to camp or whether it somehow grew in my mind on the track organically, but the visualization was there every day with me.

Silverman ran alone, I walked alone.

Frosty and Bob walked in tandem for hours doing interval pushups at the workout station. Frosty replaced Bob with Polish Steve doing far less laps but continuing the interval pushups. The Muslim car – Curry, Thing 1 and Thing 2, and Kaboom – sometimes joined by Old Joe, Wang and Not-Archie would team walk every day. The old White car would team walk invariably working out their release date calculations under the First Step Act. Of the more than 700 hours I spent walking the track during my 310 days at camp, I can remember only nine where I walked any distance with anyone and only three occasions when I walked more than one lap with a camper.

Of the 310 days I spent at Fairton, I failed to walk at all on only ten days. Of these 10, I only skipped three because I decided to take the day off. The other seven days off the track were caused by knee or foot pain that made walking simply impossible. I walked on the hottest days (July 20, 2019 when the heat index hit 118) and on the coldest (Valentine's Day, 2020 – high in the mid-30s). I walked on the rainiest days and the windiest days.

Chapter 21
Do the Hustle

Day 124. October 15, 2019

227: 42 Pounds to Go

"In the morning our breakfasts were put through the hole in the door, in small oblong-square tin, made to fit, and holding a pint of chocolate with brown bread, and an iron spoon. When they called for vessels again, I was green enough to return what bread I had left; but my comrade seized it, and said that I should lay that up for lunch or dinner."

Thoreau, Civil Disobedience, p. 12

My idea was never to work in the kitchen in the first place. When I arrived at camp, the first piece of advice I was given was to figure out a way to get out of food service. The new BOP head of the camp, Counselor West, had come to the camp just a month before I surrendered and had issued an edict that all new campers had to work their first 90 days in the kitchen. This led most of the self surrenders to scramble to secure other jobs before the kitchen cop called their number. Murder Mike secured a maintenance job, Frosty went up to landscaping where most of the older white guys landed. My skill sets gravitated, shall we say, away from the manual labor fields leaving me little opportunity to flee my fate.

Food service, if you were not a chef (and few were – certainly not yours truly), meant the following job assignments: food prep – primarily cutting vegetables; washer – cleaning trays/pots/pans/sporks; kitchen orderly – cleaning all surfaces in the kitchen itself; linebacking – in-meal support for the line servers replacing spent serving trays with filled ones from the hot box or refrigerator, replacing trays and sporks, and cleaning the line after meals; and outside orderly – cleaning tables, sweeping and mopping floors, filling the juice station, prepping the breakfast bags.

So when the kitchen cop called my number on July 14th, I was prepared. When he assigned me to kitchen orderly duties (probably the worst of all assignments as it entails scrubbing the big pots and pans and cleaning all trays) I threw the old man medical card – the nerve damage and back surgeries making the lifting of large pots and pans unmanageable. I countered with outside orderly – I could watch the news while I swept, mopped, cleaned tables and filled the juice station; the total number of hours this would take me was less than three hours a day giving me more than enough time to get back to Wilson and my walking schedule, and it would keep me out of the danger zone – the back of the kitchen.

Still the realization that a life's work at 59 years of age culminated in the mopping of floors and wiping down tables did get me down. I had to pull myself together going into the first visit with my girls preparing to tell them their father was a cafeteria orderly. But as it turns out, my time spent in food service became one of the great experiences of my camp life. The lesson I learned is as trite as it is true: if you're going to do a job – no matter how much it may depress you mentally or emotionally – put in the effort and do it well and good things can happen. I put in the effort. I did it well. And good things did happen.

First, I changed the formula for making ice tea and fruit punch. My mentor, H, showed me the ropes before he passed the beverage making baton, actually a whisk, onto me. The key to success on the beverage front was changing the mix of Aspartame-based powder to water-to-ice ratio. By reducing the powder and water and increasing the ice, the punches and teas had the sweetness that reminded me of my favorites growing up – T-Time Ice Tea and Hawaiian Punch Fruit Juice. These were the standards by which I made my beverages; they didn't go on the line until they tasted like T-Time and Hawaiian Punch.

The one beverage the guys hated most was the lemonade which smelled like a version of cleanser and tasted like a version of medicine no matter the mix ratios. So I mixed it with the ice tea powder and marketed it as the first BOP Arnold Palmer. When I couldn't mix it with tea, I mixed it with fruit punch and called it Strawberry Lemonade. Soon guys were letting me know they liked my tea – and crazy as it may sound, that made me happy.

By the Fall, as new campers came into food service, the older White guys would approach me to avoid the back of the kitchen as I had. At this point, I could have quit food service altogether having served my 90 days. As the camper number had spiked to over capacity – they were putting new arrivals in stand-alone cots by the doors in December – it was unlikely I would have been reassigned to another job before I packed out. So why didn't I leave?

Do the Hustle.

First a disclaimer. As I have explained in Shock and Awful, it took me a couple months to get my bearings as to the dos and don'ts of camp life. Even then, I was still one of the most clueless campers ever to walk through the doors of Fairton. My cluelessness was, in part, a natural by-product of my free world environment. When your survival doesn't depend on a hustle, you don't spend your days looking for those opportunities. It was also part of a conscious decision on my part to stay very much on the straight and narrow while serving my time. There was a reason I didn't switch out of the bunk closest to the cop station in Times Square even when I had the chance – craziness and contraband do not thrive when you are an arm's length at all times from a cop.

So there we are toward the end of August in Central Park, Wilson and I, minding our own business. It is a Thursday about an hour or so after lunch, say noonish. And Big John, the number 2 camper in the kitchen (the head-chef camper is Number 1), comes at me holding a brown paper bag, hands it to me and says, "Smukler, this is for you."

Prior to this moment, I had had one conversation with Big John – a leader of the Black car. That was my first day in food service some five weeks before when I ventured into the strange world of industrial mopping. At the time, I figured I knew all I needed to know about mopping – fill a bucket with hot water, stick mop head into it, ring it out through the strainer, and you were good to go. After slathering the floor with water, Big John comes up to me and says, "Smukler, you never mopped a floor before?" (I got the sense that inmates of color got a kick out of confirming just how little real world experience the White self-surrenders had coming into prison). To what we both knew to be a rhetorical question, I answered, "How could you tell?" Big John proceeded to take me through the fine art of straining a mop head – one which included twisting the mop head clockwise in the strainer three times then compressing the strainer three times to insure that as much water as possible had left the mop head before returning it to the floor. I quickly came to understand the exact water-to-mop head ratio necessary to affect the most thorough and efficient mopping. When subsequent White self-surrenders came into food service mopping, I passed this technique forward.

Beyond this tutorial, Big John and I had had no interaction. So it was a surprise that he approached our table let alone handed me a paper bag. And inside the bag was, well, nothing short of an ecstasy in plastic wrap – two chicken quarters.

As I had been working in food service for five weeks, I did not initially think that this largesse was anything more than a one-off: that morning, the kitchen cop had called all of food service in, closed the doors to the chow hall, had us move all the tables to the far end of the room, then pour liberal amounts of pink industrial strength cleaner down and scrub, squeegee, and mop the entire floor. Big John's brown paper gift was, I thought, acknowledgement of the extra effort expended in the chow hall that morning. And what a gift! Two chicken quarters was, in my protein-starved world the nicest present I could receive. Then, the following Thursday it happened again and that was the start of my food hustle.

What I came to realize, slower than most, is that there is an understanding within food service that the benefits of food service employment (if you could call it that – making $20.00/month) was access to the food service hustle – a weekly benefits program overseen by the Number One and Number 2 in the kitchen and tacitly, and some time not so tacitly, approved by the kitchen cop.

On Chicken Tuesday, extra chicken patties; some burger Wednesdays, extra burgers (though not always); two, sometimes three, chicken quarters on Thursday; and when available at dinner, extra meat loaf or extra turkey slices from the Chef Salad; some weekends, a Caribbean camper would whip up a curried fish dish; on Super Bowl Sunday, extra chicken wings.

The best part of the hustle, for me, came on Thanksgiving when the food service got first crack at the turkey which meant for me attacking the leg, thigh and wing.

[Aside: The Thanksgiving turkey rivaled the other best meal at Fairton – the July 4th barbecued chicken prepared on the industrial sized smoker parked on the loading dock behind the kitchen. One of only two times we used the smoker, the other being New Year's Day when Dan, the former kitchen Number One, put the apron back on to grill steaks for our holiday meal. I was so much a part of food service at that time, I was entrusted with the second-most important job in the camp that morning – basting the steaks pre- and post-grill with Dan's homemade steak sauce].

The protein hustle, while enhancing the amount of protein in my daily diet, was also giving me protein for barter – and that was where my food hustle began. Another lesson of Fairton: If you are given access to a food hustle, never turn your back on it. If you cannot fit the food into your diet, just find a way to hustle the hustle into another hustle. On Tuesdays, when I got extra breaded chicken patties, I hustled them to Nell and created a pizza account ensuring that I never had to pay for pizza or diet coke. When I commissioned Chief as a personal trainer, I shifted this re-hustle to him providing him extra protein for his diet in exchange for his tutelage in the weight room.

While I was a benign beneficiary of this first tier of food service hustle, the second tier of the hustle I created on my own. Here's how it happened.

Part of the portfolio for my non-kitchen-based food service job actually brought me into the kitchen to prepare the breakfast bags for distribution at dinner Sunday through Thursday.

As more campers came to Fairton, and more were conscripted into the food service, I was able to redefine the scope of my "employment" to take the mop and dish rags out of my hands and move to overseeing the breakfast bag production. This entailed placing fruit, pastry, and hot/cold cereal into 120 brown paper bags ready for delivery at the 3:00 P.M. Short Line – an operation that gave me direct access to pastry, as well as two things Milo Minderbinder coveted most – bran cereal and grapefruit.

Milo was a camper of extraordinary talents. I call him Milo as an homage to the Catch-22 character who used his war service as an opportunity to create a global for-profit business. Milo was a hustler extraordinaire. If you wanted for anything, Milo was your man. If you wanted to unload anything, Milo was your man.

My access to what Milo wanted gave me the platform for my government cheese hustle; I would leave bags of bran cereal and/or grapefruits in my locker for Milo to pick up; he would leave government cheese wrapped in plastic under my pillow. Breakfast bags also gave me access to bananas – a high value food target both for me and for barter.

My breakfast bag food hustle was the minor leagues compared to the hustle operations of those touching the food. The week after I surrendered, I was told by a camper that I just missed the egg delivery – a carton of 30 dozen eggs coming into the housing unit. Months after I arrived, the entire food warehouse operation was let go for stealing food for the camp (or so I am told). The food service workers who worked up the service road now transitioned into the kitchen which simply meant that the food hustle that originated in the warehouse now originated further down the food chain to the weekly unloading of food, the Thursday Pull, to be stored in the indoor and outdoor walk-in coolers, the walk-in freezer and the Dry Room.

My hustle was both smaller in scale and had, let's call it, plausible rationalization built into it. I rarely swiped food outright from the breakfast bag operation (the exception being green bananas). Where I hustled was from the bags that went untaken after the dinner chow line closed. Each day, with few exceptions, we prepared between 110 and 120 bags for distribution – one per man. But most days, with few exceptions, not every man made it onto the chow line for dinner: Taco Monday was never well attended – and for good reason. Of those men who did show up, not all took a breakfast bag, particularly if the bag had an apple or a choke biscuit pastry, both of which for some were considered inedible.

This left me with between 15 and 20 bags returned from the chow line to do with as I wished. I would place these bags in a box and, the next morning, decide whether to put them back out on the line the next day or rifle through them and take the high value hustle items for my personal use – primarily the cereal for Milo or Chocolate Chip/Blueberry Starbucks muffins for my personal trainer, Chief, or mini-chocolate croissants for my bunkmates in Times Square or a camper, Jay Muscle, who was seemingly addicted to them.

My plausible rationalization was that these items were bags that had been offered and rejected and, technically, per BOP rules, should have been thrown away rather than re-used for the next day's breakfast bag allotment. That was my story and I was sticking to it if ever caught. I was never caught. Not so much because I was clever or sly but because (1) I wasn't a pig about my hustle; (2) I gave far more effort to my work which was "rewarded" by the kitchen cops who gave me pretty much free reign to go where I wanted and access what I wanted just as long as I made sure the breakfast bags were completed in a timely fashion each day; and (3) my hustle was so far down on the "food hustle" chain, so to speak, that it wasn't worth bothering with – when whole sides of beef and cases of sausage are walking out the back door, a muffin or banana here or there is simply the cost of keeping an efficient breakfast bagging operation on line.

As I redefined my role into breakfast bag production, I added another role to my portfolio: linebacking.

Linebacking spiked the food hustle, as there was food beyond the protein hustle described above that I now had access to, particularly extra salad and non-regularly scheduled lunch protein like tuna fish (on Friday, of course). As the linebackers carted the unused portions of the serving trays back into the kitchen for re-use at a later meal or throwaway, opportunities abounded to grab what I wanted for personal consumption or hustle.

[Aside: The amount of food the BOP throws away at each meal could feed entire neighborhoods of Philadelphia: whole serving trays of rice, beans, potatoes, and canned vegetables of all kinds were regularly carted back to the cleaning station to be ditched into the trash. It was not unusual to see whole trays of some protein, particularly the "beef" taco, get dumped as well.

This is not the fault of the linebackers who received clearance to dump these trays into the trash. Nor is it the fault of the kitchen cops who are required to prepare enough food to meet the posted menu requirements at each meal; if you must, by regulation, make enough beef taco, beans, and rice for 120 guys and only 60 guys show up for the meal, you are creating waste by fiat.

The overall number of food-insecure individuals in New Jersey is close to ten percent of the state's population. A 2018 study by the Reinvestment Fund, a policy and investment organization focusing on low-income communities, found that as of 2016, 879,188 New Jersey residents were living in limited supermarket-access areas. During my last weeks at camp, when the pandemic became real and folks were lining up for food in South Jersey, we continued to dump hundreds of pounds of food per week into the trash which is, at best, non-sensical and at worst – shameless].

One last benefit for me in staying in this newly defined food service role – camper interaction.

As I have laid out through this memoir, solitude is a critical component to repurposing your mind for short-term significant weight loss on the Jailbird Diet. I was not engaging in or seeking out any camper-to-camper conversations nor placing myself into physical spaces where such interactions took place. It was me and Wilson and nobody else.

While this well-defined solitude placed my mind and body in a posture well-tuned for hunger avoidance, it was a lonely existence. Your body and mind lose the craving for food but begin to crave the sustenance of human interaction.

My food service role overseeing breakfast bags allowed me to slake this new kind of hunger. Each day at the 3:00 P.M. Short Line, I would stand at the spork and tray station leading into the chow line serving stations handing each camper his breakfast bag.

Campers would ask what was in the bag and I began a running joke, describing the contents as though it were the breakfast at a five-star hotel: the choke biscuit became a "personalized oatmeal cinnamon scone with just a hint of nutmeg;" the rotten apple became "a hand-picked Pink Lady from Washington State's Yakima Valley" (just making this shit up as I went). During football season, I would play quarterback throwing breakfast bags across the chow hall to guys waiting deep in the chow line or go down the line handing them off like a quarterback to his running back. I would have separate brown bags of single serve oatmeal ready to hand to those guys I knew valued them; gave a second bag on the down-low to those I wanted/needed to take care of; grabbed some brown sugar from the Dry Room for those who asked (and I wanted to help). In short, I became a go-to for others seeking to expand their diets through fruits, pastry, and cereal that I had access to.

My food service camper interaction was not always a Kumbaya coming together moment. When a new worker came in under my portfolio to line-back and tried to scam the system, I got him fired. This was dicey as I never knew who that camper was tied to, perhaps another camper who felt like my fucking with his buddy was tantamount to fucking with him. Then there was the time I used my food service to pay back a camper for what I considered to be a personal affront. It went down like this.

At night in the housing unit, from 4:00 P.M. to 7:30 A.M. campers on bottom bunks were allowed hang sheets or towels from the upper bunk down to below their beds; this was done by having Le Carre take bootlace strings and configure a clothesline underneath the side-rails of the upper bunk. The only caveat was that these sheets/towels when put up had to leave enough of a gap to allow the nighttime cop (on at 10:00 P.M. out at 6:00 A.M.) to see into the bunk with his flashlight for the 12:30, 3:30 and 5:00 A.M. counts. I always pushed my sheet and towel coverage to the limit to provide me with maximum privacy. At the foot of my bad, I had my winter coat, sweat pants and sweat shirt, and bags of clean and dirty clothes hung in such a way as to obscure sight lines from the highly trafficked walkway between my bed and the cop station enhancing what I called the "I Dream of Genie" effect.

One night, the night watchman – Weisman – didn't take kindly to my privacy concerns and proceeded at the 12:30 count to rip down my sheet, towels and clothing and dump them at the foot of my bed. Awakened to find my property lying on the walkway at the foot of my bed, I look down the bunk line to see a camper three bunks down, let's call him Skeeter, laughing at my predicament: "Yuk Yuk…hey Weisman you really fucked Smukler's stuff up…Yuk Yuk."

Skeeter was a night owl, some called it doing drug time – a camper that stayed up all night and slept all day. For these campers, a good relationship with the night cop meant something; the night cop could turn the TVs off any time he wanted to, shutting down access to the chow hall and leaving the night owls to hang out in the bathroom. For me, the night cop meant nothing as I slept through the night.

Fast forward to the chow line next day when I am doing something I did only a handful of times at camp – serve food to the campers in line. This day, for a reason I cannot recall, the kitchen was short on servers so I handed my breakfast bag station off to another camper and took the tongs to hand out salad.

And here comes Skeeter down the line. I say nothing to him and give him his salad. Ten minutes later here comes Skeeter again for seconds. As you now know, giving or denying seconds is entirely up to the server. So I gave Skeeter a piece of my mind.

Smukler: "You want more salad? You're asking *me* for more salad? Why don't you go ask Weisman for my salad?"

Skeeter's response: "Watch your mouth, Smukler."

Smukler: "See if you can get salad from your buddy Weisman cause you sure as hell ain't getting any more salad from me."

Skeeter: "I said watch your fucking mouth, Smukler."

Smukler: "Watch my mouth? No. You watch your fucking mouth. Maybe you'll think twice before yucking it up with Weisman when he dumps my stuff on the floor."

Then it was over. Skeeter walked away and, after the Short Line closed shop, I went to my table to hang out for the Main Line after the 4:00 P.M. count. Then a most unlikely camper came up to me. Big Bill – shot caller of the White Car and a man mountain, let's say 6–8, 350 pounds – stands over me and tells me that he heard I got into it with Skeeter. I told him that I only did so because Skeeter had sided with the night cop when he pulled my stuff down and I didn't think a camper should ever side with a cop against another camper for any reason. Big Bill's response: "Skeeter's just a kid, he's 23 years old." My response; "That's old enough to know not to take the side of a cop against a camper."

And that is where it ended. Weeks later, Skeeter came up to me to ask me if I had gotten my out date from the case manager, I said I had, and he fist bumped me and that's when I knew we were good. And I felt relieved.

Moral of the story: Pick your battles very carefully. I had been in camp for months and, though I remained pretty much to myself, my food service position and the hustles it created, forged close ties with shot callers across the White, Black, and Spanish cars. If Skeeter wanted to put a hurt on me, which he could easily have done, it would have been at his peril as those who would have revenged my pain could clearly have inflicted any amount of pain they wanted on Skeeter. He and I both knew where we stood so it died where it should have died. Thank God.

Chapter 22
The Demon Baker of Eat Street

Day 186. December 17, 2019
210: 25 Pounds to Go

My stint as maître d' of the breakfast bags led to one of the more dramatic transformations of my life inside the camp – one that took me far away from any experience I had in the free world and one that almost deep-sixed any hopes to achieve significant weight loss while I was away.

It was born out of a simple observation of camper behavior over weeks of breakfast bag deliveries. As I took over the bagging operation, the food service warehouse had a glut of pastries that were known as "choke biscuits:" individually wrapped scone-shaped pastries that would crumble into a rough powder when bitten into and, therefore choke-inducing, if not consumed with milk.

When the food service warehouse has a glut of something, its solution is to keep throwing it at the campers until the glut is gone and that is exactly how they handled choke biscuits. For days and days and then weeks, the breakfast bags would have choke biscuits as their pastry du jour. On the other hand, the campers would deal with this glut as you might expect: discard the choke biscuit either in the trash or by placing it on the microwave table – the food version of a Lost and Found – or decline the breakfast bag altogether.

This colossal waste of food began to get to me. I had worked in the hunger space in the free world developing a hybrid supermarket in the food desert of Chester PA and, though by no means a poster boy for food waste prevention, still was rankled by the absurdity of a situation in which the BOP knew it was serving food that was being thrown away yet did nothing to halt the practice.

So if the BOP wasn't going to deal with this problem, I gamed out a way to handle it myself.

At the beginning of the third week straight of choke biscuits, I executed the plan: when the men came through the line, I asked those who took their bags if they wanted their choke biscuit. To those who responded in the negative, I would ask if I could take their choke biscuit from the bag, leaving them with the hot/cold cereal and the fruit. I would then place the biscuits into a separate box I had placed by the tray/spork station where we handed out the breakfast bags. Then, at the end of breakfast bag distribution, I would take all the unclaimed bags, remove their biscuits, and add to my collection. After a week of collections, I had a full box of biscuits – nearly 100 to work with.

I was now ready to approach the kitchen cop.

As I said in the Chapter 2, Shock and Awful, one of the worst parts of the camping experience is the mercurial nature of the cops – you never knew what you were going to get; while on one side of the coin were the SIS who put the 'I' in SS, the other side were the cops who treated campers like human beings; those who looked upon their work as campers looked upon themselves with dignity and just tried to make each day go by as quickly and painlessly as possible. O was one such cop.

I met O in the first week of my stay and he provided me with camp insight that I never lost sight of during my time at Fairton and which will stay with me for the rest of my life.

Here's how it happened.

I surrendered at camp on a Monday. By the following Saturday, four days in I was still getting my bearings or at least thought I was. While the lights did not come on at 6:00 A.M. as on the weekdays, I still was up and out of bed at 6:00 and headed out of the housing unit toward the chow hall with Wilson and my reading materials in hand. As this was my first Saturday, I did not realize that the food schedule was different, milk was not brought out of the kitchen between 6:00 and 6:15 but was brought out when the breakfast chow line (which only happened Saturdays and Sundays) ramped up at 7:30.

As I stood at the chow hall double doors, I looked to my left toward the hallway double doors that constituted the main entrance to Fairton camp. I could see the sun streaming through the door's windows so I decided I would take Wilson, place him just outside the front doors, face the East to bask in what was a glorious morning sunrise, and read the New York Times – just as

I would do each Saturday morning in the free world – life was bad, but not so bad if you could read the NYT outside in the summer while watching the sunrise.

And here comes O.

O: "What the hell do you think you're doing?"

Smukler: "Just sitting here reading my paper."

O: "Get the hell inside the building."

Smukler: "But I saw other guys standing here yesterday morning at this time so I thought it was OK."

O: "Man your lucky you got me as CO today and not someone else; they would have given your ass a shot before you hit the door."

["Shots" are the penalty system through which the BOP disciplines inmates ranging from the lowest 400 series – say smoking cigarettes or hustling food – to 100 series – getting caught out of bounds moving contraband.]

So I picked up Wilson and walked back into the hallway then into the chow hall and sat in the spot I had designated for myself the previous four breakfasts at the table just outside the kitchen door. A few minutes later O comes out of the kitchen (the kitchen cop has his/her own office just inside the kitchen door to the left so they can see all traffic coming in and, more importantly for hustle purposes, going out of the kitchen at all times) looks at me and tells me to come into his office.

O: "What's your name?"

Smukler: "Smukler"

O: "This is your first time in prison, Smukler, am I right?"

Smukler: "Yes. Is it that obvious?"

O: "Yeah. It's pretty damn obvious. How long you in for?"

Smukler: "I was sentenced to 18 months."

O: "OK Smukler I am gonna give you two pieces of advice I want you to remember while you are here with us."

"First, never go outside and sit in a place where no other campers are sitting. If you're outside and no other campers are around, there is a pretty good chance that you're sitting in the wrong place at the wrong time.

Second, when a CO asks you why you are doing something, never and I mean NEVER, explain yourself by saying that you saw other campers doing the same thing. That is not because the CO will have a problem with you telling him that, it is a problem because they – and he pointed to the campers through his window sitting in the chow hall – will have a problem with it."

On a few occasions I gave these pearls of wisdom to other self-surrenders who were as clueless as I coming into camp. It's also not a bad piece of advice to carry with you in the free world.

Now back to the biscuits.

My idea was to take the biscuits out of their individual wrappers, crumble them into a 4" baking pan – not difficult as they were, after all, choke biscuits. Then wing it. And when I say wing it, I mean make it up as I go because I had zero baking skills up to that very moment.

In fact, in the free world I was the anti-baking guy. Whenever Shelly would suggest baking anything, sweet or savory it did not matter, I would respond with: "We have a hundred bakeries within miles of our home. These bakers are paid professionals. Why would we ever want to bake anything when all the baked goods we love are waiting fresh at our beck and call within a few minutes' drive. Oh and by the way, there is no post-baking cleanup operation required" (this last point was most important as Shelly would not conscript me into the baking operation but she would sure as hell grab me for the cleaning).

I only knew one thing about baking for sure – you couldn't go wrong with butter and sugar – and the kitchen held each of these ingredients in large quantities. My idea was to keep it as simple as possible: use the crumbled biscuits as the crust, so to speak, for a cobbler. I had stumbled into this idea the week earlier when I walked into the shed – a stand-alone structure sitting on the loading dock off the back of the kitchen that houses the surplus for the in-kitchen dry room: bags of flour, rice, paper products, beverage mix, cereals etc. – and there they sat: cases of fruit pie filling.

You know, the kind of filling used in the pies that sit in the cases at your favorite Greek diner: cherry, strawberry, blueberry (which came in an oddly marked can called "Pizza Topping") and my absolute favorite – apple cinnamon (which tasted eerily like the filling of my favorite Tastykake growing up – Dutch Apple Pie).

So now all I had to do was add butter (really margarine because the BOP did not bring butter into the kitchen), some milk and some sugar to the crumbled biscuits to turn them into a moist paste-like crust then put the pans into the oven to get the crust a little toasty; take the crispy crust out after say 20 minutes at 250, then liberally apply the pie filling of choice on top of the crust. All that left was the topping. So I asked O for help.

The beauty of O was not only that he cared and took pride in the kind of food he served the men (not something I could say about all of the kitchen cops) but he also truly liked to bake (something I could say about no other kitchen cop).

O handed me a handwritten recipe for a crumb topping: rolled oats, flour, margarine, and brown sugar. I followed it then liberally spread the topping over my pans of pie filling laying on top of the choke biscuit crust and voila! Smukler's Choke Biscuit Cobbler.

My cobblers were a hit. In part because they were desserts added to a weekly menu in which dessert was a planned menu item on Tuesdays and Thursdays and no other days. I am pretty sure if we had thrown anything out on the line that combines the amounts of sugar, flour, and margarine I was using and called it dessert the men would have been grateful. When you have pretty much the same basic menu every day going on for year after year, any deviation is immediately noticed and appreciated.

So I moved into different cobblers. When the guys started getting tired of choke biscuits, I went to the Krispy Kreme honey buns – delicious but at over 400 calories a pop not the kind of delicious that guys would pound for breakfast more than two days in a row – when they tired of them, I prepared them into a crust and paired them with cherry pie filling and the go-to crumble topping. The apple cinnamon I paired with leftover spice cake.

Initially, my foray into the baking arena was just an attempt to solve the problem of the discarded choke biscuits; I had no intention of increasing my presence in the kitchen. My food hustle was going well and my days outside of the chow hall were with Wilson in Central Park filled with reading, walking, and cross-wording.

But the Fall, which had been pretty dry and mild, was now turning to Winter. To hold fast to Silverman's sage advice – stay outside as much as possible – was much easier for Silverman than it was for me: he had a "full-time" job down the service road doing paperwork for the food warehouse. The only indoor venue that would keep me out of the housing unit on days when it was too cold to sit outside was the chow hall. I had cased out a standalone table in the corner which I could have declared as mine, much as I declared the table in Central Park from the day I placed Wilson and my reading/writing materials at it. But the chow hall was only a bit less suffocating than the housing unit. The televisions were always on which meant there were always campers milling about; and the space was too confined to give me the same separation and solitude I had in the park. I needed to find a space inside where I could be alone in between the hours I spent walking on the track. And if that meant I couldn't read and write, then so be it but it would have to be a space in which I could keep challenging my brain.

The solution? Become the Baker of Fairton.

While my choke biscuit initiative gave me entree to the baking operation, what sealed my fate was, like so much that happened at camp, the lack of any one to stop me. The kitchen staff was shorthanded to begin with. The departure of the Number 1, Dan, to the food warehouse after the warehouse purge left a void which was filled by Big Mike who was one of those relieved of duties at the warehouse in the Monday Morning Massacre. The Number 2 was the Imam, Mr. 505 was Number 3. Wu was veggie prep. None of them was interested in handling the baking responsibilities. Not-Archie had offered his services but he was the one I got fired for failure to put the time in.

So I gradually worked my way into the spot. First, by handling the baking for the breakfast bags. As there is a pastry requirement for 120 bags, five days a week, there is always some level of baking necessary: mini chocolate croissants (both campers and cops enjoyed ribbing me for the way I pronounced croissant, so I ended up calling them chocolate-filled pastry), generic honey buns (non-Krispy Kreme), apple fritters, and cookies all required panning and heating up before being individually wrapped for the breakfast bags. So that was my first baby step into baking. On top of the breakfast bags, the BOP expected the kitchen to prepare breakfast cakes for the men to be served in the breakfast chow line on Saturday and Sunday as well other cakes for the scheduled desserts on Tuesday and Thursday. So O gave me his handwritten recipe using the yellow cake mix as the base then jazzing it up as he or I saw fit.

And that's when I started to learn how to bake: separate wet from dry then add the sugar, regulate your mixing speeds, scrape the batter off the sides of the mixing bowl before your batter is fully mixed, don't fuck up the baking powder and baking soda (which I did), make sure you add the vanilla extract (which I forgot), pour out three sheet pans to the correct height on the pan so it doesn't overflow in the oven (which it did more than once).

Another quality of O was that even when I fucked up, he let me do a workaround. And sometimes my fuck ups actually turned out to really surprise: Like the time I used pancake mix flour instead of regular flour only realizing my mistake when I started dusting the pans to prep them for the batter. As any real baker knows, dusting a pan is simply greasing it then sprinkling flour onto the greased pan to make a dusting. When I sprinkled the wrong flour onto the greased pan, it started to crumble – something that had never happened in previous dustings. Sensing something was wrong, I went back to the 50 lb. bag of flour in the dry room only to realize my mistake – using pancake flour rather than cake flour. I told O whose response was, "Let's see what happens." Turned out my new pancake flour-yellow cake mix was a hit; it did something I could never make happen using regular flour – the cake fluffed up while retaining its moisture. Who knew?

Once I had the cobbler thing down, I began to branch out into new and, like everything for me in the kitchen, unchartered, territory. The Imam taught me how to make icing out of confectionary sugar, margarine, milk, and his own secret recipe – a dash of salt at the very end of the mixing. Big Mike taught me the secret of nuking the pre-made cream cheese icing and 505 the icing bag technique. When we got giant apples (I swear if apple growth hormones are a thing, these were packing them), I took a spork and cored them (turns out the BOP plastic sporks are the perfect utensil for coring apples), added margarine, brown sugar and some granola (not my idea but that of the kitchen cop, Cujo, who like O took an interest in my baking adventures).

One day as I was in the walk-in cooler, I brought a box down that had been wedged into the far upper corner; it contained a large bag of pitted dates which I used to make a date bread with date icing. After some investigation, I found out that the dates had been delivered over a year earlier as part of the BOP's culinary celebration of Ramadan (if dates have a shelf life in a cooler, I can now say with some certainty, it is greater than one year).

[Aside: The BOP's culinary approach to religious holidays showed a largesse that, I am sure, would come as a surprise to most in the free world. The most extravagant meal I ever saw prepared was during the Christmas season (but not Christmas) in honor of a saint no one could name. It included beef, poultry, lasagna, four sides, and cake, pie, and ice cream for dessert.

The Jewish car, as we have seen, had its weekly challah and grape juice but also a killer 7-day 20-meal Passover. The Rastas had a special jerk chicken meal. The Muslims were taken care of on Ramadan. The only group I didn't see get at least one special meal was the Wiccans but they did get firewood and matches to light their Winter Solstice bonfire.]

What put my baking career, such that it was, on steroids was my discovery of whipped cream – or I should say the liquid ingredient that makes whipped cream; half gallon replicas of a single-serve milk carton that came in vanilla and chocolate flavoring. Just dump the contents into the industrial mixer, set to Level 1 – the lowest mix level – for about ten minutes then jack up the speed to Level 3 for five minutes and you've got what was tantamount to culinary crack for the campers. Once discovered, there was no putting that genie back in the bottle. I put whipped cream on everything: cobblers, cakes, the old-fashioned red jello with fruit in it, on top of a product we got called 7-layer brownies (I tried once to figure out the 7 but only came up with six – (1) a blonde brownie with (2) chocolate fudge, (3) chocolate chips, (4) butterscotch, (5) butterscotch chips, and (6) coconut flakes – all my favorite foods packed into one dessert!).

O liked to make pudding which was no problem as we had cases of both chocolate and vanilla powdered pudding mix. One day we made a multi-layered vanilla and chocolate pudding creation separated by cookie crumbles – we would get boxes of 200 pre-cut frozen chocolate espresso or sugar walnut cookies which I would pan up and bake; as the Black Car only liked them prepared in soft chewy state, those that ventured toward the crisp were left over for repurposing. Then add a couple layers of bananas. I called it The Cosby as it was like the pudding pops, he hawked on television in the 1970s – I may or may not have made reference when serving it on the line to his putting his banana in vanilla and chocolate. This became the most popular dessert served during my brief but illustrious career. I even went so far as to take a chocolate pudding, put it on top of the 7-layer brownies then top it with, you guessed it, whipped cream and called it Death by Chocolate.

Then the Thursday Pull brought into the Dry Room a 50-pound bag of Reese's peanut butter. I made peanut butter cookies, peanut butter icing to top a chocolate cake, and the ultimate – a peanut butter and jelly (technically strawberry pie filling but you get the point) cobbler on top of re-purposed breakfast brownie crust.

Whipped cream was so beloved by the campers that it could save even the most disastrous of my failures in the baking world – and let me assure you, there were many: typically disasters were cakes that overflowed in the oven because I filled the sheet pans too high or cakes that didn't rise high enough because I added too much fruit to the recipe. My greatest whip cream save was the time I made two sheet pans of basic yellow cake neither of which rose more than an inch off the bottom of the sheet pan (no doubt a baking powder/soda error). I let them cool off while I prepared an industrial bowl of vanilla whipped cream. I then spread the whipped cream over one sheet pan of yellow cake, flipped the other sheet pan of yellow cake on top of its now whipped creamed sister then whipped creamed the top layer on top of which I sprinkled some of the left-over crispy espresso chocolate cookies.

It was my dream to revisit this concoction in my last days at camp using the strawberry pie filling and strawberry icing to make a strawberry short cake – one of my faves and also the cake that Shelly and I celebrated with on our wedding day. Alas, I packed out too suddenly to make this dream a reality.

Baking for me became part of my new identity. O would get on the PA system before the Short Line and advertise my desserts, "Tonight is Smukler's Special Pudding on the Short Line." I put myself into the serving line whenever my dessert came out which gave me another point of interaction with the camp and allowed me to take care of everyone I wanted to take care of by throwing them a bigger scoop or a second helping. A quarter of the campers would eat every dessert I had to offer; half would take some but limited their intake; and a quarter would deny any dessert not because they didn't want it but because they couldn't pay the price – and for good reason.

[Aside: As we have seen at 5:45 A.M. the housing cop would unlock the health office (stationed off the hallway between the housing unit and the chow hall directly across from the bathroom) for the Pill Line. This was repeated at 3:30 P.M., Roughly 20% of the men at Fairton required some form of medication on a daily basis to primarily deal with high blood pressure and sugar levels; heart disease and diabetes were the two greatest threats to inmates' health. Both conditions were exacerbated by the sugars and fats I loaded into my desserts.]

Assuming the baker's apron allowed me to achieve three important goals: (1) I spent hours off by myself creating, learning, studying, and experimenting – challenging my brain and body in ways that I had never challenged myself

160

before; (2) it gave me the solitude I craved – the solitude I could no longer insure by my separation with Wilson in the park now that the Winter cold had arrived; and (3) it provided me another point of social interaction with campers in an environment where I spent almost every hour by myself.

And the feedback was, quite frankly, exhilarating. I now get why bakers bake. Hearing someone thank you for preparing a dessert that they enjoyed is a very powerful, personally validating experience: one I looked forward to each time I brought out one of my desserts.

And then I quit.

I quit for one reason: baking was stalling out my weight loss program.

I was a baker who tasted everything…at every stage of the baking process. From swiping the whipped cream off the mixing bowl paddle as I was taking it back to the clean area to the batter in the mixing bowl to the time the cobbler or cake came out of the oven to the time I was bringing the goodies back off the chow line to the time it was sitting in the dessert pantry the next morning, I was licking and nibbling all the time. Peanut butter, chocolate, pudding, chocolate and butterscotch chips, the bottom of the cake sheet pans where the greasiest part to the cake remains, I was licking or nibbling at all of these.

While I would never sit down and have a piece of anything I made, I came to realize I was consuming large quantities of sugar and fat that I refused to record each day in my logs. These tastings were not driven by hunger but by opportunity – an opportunity to indulge in little bits and pieces of yum all day long. When I committed to losing 100 pounds, I hung up my baker's apron – for good.

Chapter 23
Weight Wait Don't Tell Me

Day 205. January 6, 2020

206: 21 Pounds to Go

In 1996, an amendment to a federal appropriations bill expressly barred the federal Bureau of Prisons from purchasing "training equipment for boxing, wrestling, judo, karate, or other martial art, or any bodybuilding or weightlifting equipment of any sort." This legislation was in response to lobbying from the union representing federal correctional officers who feared that prisoners were becoming too muscled-up on weightlifting thereby presenting more of a physical threat to its members; not coincidentally, it followed on the heels of the 1994 Clinton Crime Bill – the federal response to a decade-long increase in violent crime rates that instituted a "three strikes" mandatory life sentence for repeat offenders, money to hire 100,000 new police officers, and $9.7 billion in funding for prisons.

In every federal correctional institution there is a weight room (so I am told). Fairton was no exception.

The weight room was an indoor-outdoor affair: an A-frame 15' × 25' situated just off the back deck of the housing unit. The open ceiling is wooden cross beamed, the floor a series of connecting rubberized pads. The weights come in many shapes and sizes: bars used in single pulley universal machines; barbells ranging from 20 pounds to 60 pounds, bars of 45 and 65 pounds with discs (nickels, dimes, quarters and 45s). The machines ring the perimeter of the structure moving counterclockwise from the door. I never asked the names of these machines though I assume each had one but did know them by muscles group they attacked: back – you sit on the floor and pull weight to chest; chest – sit in the machine raise arms to side at right angles then pull weights in from side to in front of face; further down the northern wall were the single arm barbells and bars for bench and clean-and-jerk lifting; in the far corner the leg machines for quads, hamstrings and calves. In the middle of the far wall was a platform for lifting in front of a full-length mirror; in the far-left corner two arm machines for shoulders, triceps, and biceps. In the middle of the room were one bench, two incline benches and a tree holding the disc weights. Along the left wall were two stationary bikes (these were brought in during my stay – an exception to the federal ban on new equipment as cardio – not lifting machines – were upgradable) another bench with a mirror then a shoulder machine; sit in front of weights with pulley directly above your head and pull down and toward you. In the near left corner is a grapple hook attached to the ceiling where guys did chin ups then back to the door for the back machine; get in a linebacker stance and pull weights up to your chest. Along the walls were the hooks, clamps, and handlebars that were attached to the pulleys to diversify the routines. At the door was a third stationary bike and a large pre-boom-box-era radio that provided music to the room.

The equipment was treated with the respect of an old relative invited for a holiday meal – physically coddled and recognized as being from a different era. When nothing can ever be replaced, campers were expected to treat the irreplaceable with care. One day a screaming match erupted from the gym. The White big boy car – Big Bill, Ben, and Fat Bobby – joined by the Black car's self-described "Mr. 505" (an amount of weight he lifted) – were in the weight room for their regularly scheduled midday session – a time when Wilson and I would routinely hear their grunts, moans, and screams – "MUSCLE FUCK THAT WEIGHT!" – that ranged from motivational to masochistic. But this screaming was different.

The Big I, sitting at the outdoor White table, heard it as well and went to check out the commotion. He reported back that Mr. 505 had been straddling one of the benches lifting more weight than he could handle. Fat Bobby was spotting him at the time calling him pussy when 505 dropped the bar and the weight it was carrying onto the bench thereby bending the bar. Big I came back to the table and said nonchalantly that if that had happened in the Medium, Mr. 505 would have had to receive medical treatment for the type of injuries he would have sustained for breaking a piece of equipment in the weight room.

It wasn't that the equipment was old, it looked downright primeval – none more so than the leg press. You lay on your back on the floor with your legs pressed upward to a wood and metal platform. Beyond the platform at the back of the machine are the weights your legs will be pressing – for me that meant three 45-pound discs levered through a pulley to the platform. Your hands would clasp two levers, one each by your side, that would release the lock that was keeping the platform from sliding down the diagonal rails and crushing your pelvis (should your legs give out). The platform is now free to slide up and down the diagonal rails running from the floor to the top of the machine. It slides because of the black oily goo slathered on the rails allowing the platform to come down when your knees are brought to your chest and move upward when you extend your legs to a straight and locked position.

Of course, all of this was unchartered territory for me so much so that when lying prone inside the leg press, I decided to take my finger and discover what the black substance was on the rail above my right hand. Finding it to be an oily goo now on my fingers, I immediately wiped it on my gray gym sweatpants leaving a mark that would permanently remind me of why it took me six months to enter this torture chamber in the first place. But even stupidity can be rewarded at the camp.

Later that week, KeeKay of the Spanish car sees me in the chow hall and says, "Mr. Smukler, I see that you are working out. You got the black mark on your sweats." He then gives me the international thumbs up sign of approval. Moral of the tale: The guys all razzed me when I entered the gym from the very first time I entered the gym and every time thereafter; it was understood this was their domain, not mine. But if you put in the effort, they will respect you for the work, help you every step of the way, and encourage you as they would one in their car. In short, they respected the work I put in regardless of the level of weight or lack of experience I brought to the workout.

That I would ever be in a position to describe the leg press or any other aspect of the weight room was not a forgone conclusion when I arrived at camp. I was never comfortable in any weight room – not in high school or college, not as a young man, and certainly not as a middle-aged man carrying around 285 now 225 pounds. And this weight room was far from the user-friendly body image centers promoted by the free-world life fitness industry of the twenty-first century.

I peeked into the room when Scottie gave me my first tour of the camp. I saw all I needed to see to know that I would not be venturing into this area any time soon. It was too small, too dark, too dingy, too smelly and too loud to become a part of my new life. While I would not venture in there for another six months, it was very much a part of the lives of many of the men who called camp home.

In a world where personal space is treated as sacrosanct, the weight room was the place where it mattered most; the space was simply too small to handle the number of men regularly placing demands upon it. While larger institutions had a far more regimented system of scheduling (resembling that of a starter system at a golf club where times are booked and better times are paid for…or so I am told), no one entered the weight room at the spur of the moment. Once inside, no one took a bar or used a machine without clearing it with the other cars that were using the room. And the room was generally used in groups or cars rather than by solo enthusiasts. Of the 120 men at the camp, two-thirds spent some time weight lifting. If I was going to ever enter this room, I was not going to enter it alone. I was going to need a chaperone, a personal trainer if you will, to get me across the line.

Chief was an outlier. By any matrix, an outlier. A former decorated military intelligence officer and FBI officer. The son of a Native American soldier killed in Vietnam before he was born, placed on the steps of a church in New York City ultimately to be adopted by a soldier that served with his father in Vietnam. Incarcerated in the federal Super Max in Colorado, ADX Florence, known as the "Alcatraz of the Rockies."

Chief was a physical outlier as well. The strongest guys in the camp pound for pound were in their 30s and 40s – the White car's TP and Big I, the Black car's Chuck T, Boog and Little Big Man, the Spanish car's Juice, and Asian car's Tim – all were ten years younger than Chief or more. A bunch of the White car gym rats were older – in their 50s and 60s – only one who could push big weight and he blew out his gall bladder doing just that.

[Full disclosure: Of all the guys in the weight room, I pushed the least amount of weight. This was no secret in the camp (as nothing ever is). I would wear it as a badge of honor yelling as I entered the weight room: "All right boys, it's time to throw around some nickels and dimes (5- and 10-pound weights – the lightest available). I was so pathetic I started bench pressing the bar by itself. I also didn't care one bit.]

Chief was a beast. Carved upper body and legs with a belly (as most guys had) but not fat by any stretch. A buzzcut hairline. The ability to bench, lift, and shrug (shoulder lift) at the top 10% of the class. And he was my age!

He was also an outlier for his acumen around the weight room. Don't get me wrong, there was no shortage of guys who would tell you what to do in the weight room; just as many who thought they knew all there was to know about lifting. But none knew this body of science like Chief. His knowledge of the skeletal and muscular makeup of the human body coupled with the weight lifting techniques that would maximize strength and tone one muscle at a time was second to none at the camp and, I suspect, could only be replicated by paid professionals in the free world.

This expertise may or may not have been honed by his years of service in U.S. intelligence and the F.B.I. which, may or may not, have included Green Beret training which, may or may not, have included experience as a torture victim. I'll never know, it's all classified (or so I am told). I can tell you this. If Chief wanted to kill you with his bare hands, the question is not whether or not he could, but which of the 20 ways he would employ to facilitate the job. His choreography of the "suicide" murder of Jeffrey Epstein in the Manhattan Detention Center was as technically detailed as it was horrifying.

[Note: If you took a poll of the campers on the question of whether Epstein committed suicide or was murdered, they would respond to a man that there was no way he took his own life. Those who had travelled through MDC would even take you through how Epstein could have wound up without a camera on him or guards checking up on him every 30 minutes.]

If all things in life really do happen for a reason, Chief came from the Super Max in Colorado to the Camp in South Jersey to carry me across the weight room threshold; to give me the courage to enter where I refused to even step foot in the first 180 days of my captivity: my Charon ferrying me across the river Styx; my Virgil playing tour guide through the circles of Dante's Hell. Ok a bit of hyperbole but you get the point: If not for Chief, there would have been no workout program for me at Fairton. He prodded me through November and December offering to play the role of personal trainer if I would just let him take me through it. I finally acceded to the offer agreeing to start my workouts on January 1, 2020 – a new year, a new me.

For me, Chief became the keys to the kingdom. He laid out my daily routine, set up the equipment for me, explained which muscle or muscle group we would be working and how the exercise impacted that particular muscle group. Perhaps most importantly, coming into the weight room under Chief's protection allayed the regulars' concerns that I would get in their way or in any way slow them down.

We had set the time of the workout for when Chief returned to the camp from his job at UniCorp at 2:30 each weekday. I soon found out that Chief was not just the leader of his own car at their regularly scheduled 7:00 P.M. slot but was the guru for any car at any time he was in the weight room. 2:30 was ideal for me as it was a relatively unpopular time for workouts being wedged between when campers got off work and the early dinner chow line that queued up 30 minutes later at 3:00 P.M. The Big Lift car – BB, Big I, Jay Muscles, and Mr. 505 (he had left/was kicked off the Big White car depending on who you believed) started at 1:00 P.M. and would end up around 2:45 leaving just the Spanish car – Juice, Angel, and sometimes Rios – and some solo operators (solo operators were allowed at times of limited use): Skeeter, White Joe, Pompadour, and Jaws.

I quickly came to realize that going one-on-one with Chief was not ideal; I needed to form a car so that I could space out my lifts in the 45-minute workout. Enter Wang and Murder Mike.

Murder Mike.

In Times Square across from my bunk on the other side of the main drag that ran from the double doors leading into the housing unit to the cop station, was Murder Mike. Like me, he had started in the upper bunk and rotated down when his bunky packed out. Like me, he took the unusual position of deciding to stay in a Times Square lower bunk and did not attempt to relocate to the suburbs. He got the name Murder Mike because he was simply the nicest guy in the camp. One example:

My upper berth bunky (I had five during my stay not because of me but because my upper bunk was one of the worst locations in the unit – upper and in Times Square – driving all comers to seek other upper berths anywhere in the unit). My third upper bunky, we'll call him P2, came into camp complaining of gastro-intestinal issues. To be blunt, he was shitting blood.

After eight weeks in misery, he was finally taken outside the prison for tests which found rectal cancer. The plan laid out by BOP health service (an oxymoron), was to have P2 spend the next six weeks going back and forth from the camp to the hospital for chemotherapy treatments then rest for six weeks after which, if the tumor had reduced in size sufficiently, surgically remove it – all while living and sleeping at the camp.

Clearly P2, under this regimen, could not stay in his upper bunk. While he was cleared for a lower bunk, P2, like most campers, did not want to bust a lower bunky out of a lower bunk and into an upper bunk to accommodate his needs, so he was stuck. Until Murder Mike stepped in and did the unthinkable – volunteered to take P2s upper bunk putting P2 across the road in his lower bunk (no one and I mean no one but Murder Mike would do this. Heck, I was P2s lower bunky and I wouldn't do it!).

Chief and Mike were neighbors. Their nightly banter before lights out – mostly Chief busting on Murder Mike's life story, which was as much of an open book in the neighborhood as any of the Kardashians – would leave me smiling as I went to bed. To Murder Mike's credit, he could and would dish it out as good as he got.

Across from Chief's bunk was Wang – the name Chief gave him simply because he was Asian and Chief refused to ever use any other name for him in the weight room or anywhere else in the camp for that matter.

[Aside: Chief was a practical joker. In the first few weeks of my stay, Chief played one such joke on me. At 5:00 P.M. every weekday the cop would distribute the mail to the camp. This procedure required campers who were expecting mail to queue up around the cop station while the cop would call out the recipient's name, piece by piece. In preparation for incarceration, I subscribed to three daily newspapers – Philadelphia Inquirer, New York Times, and Wall Street Journal – and three monthly magazines – People, Sports Illustrated and the New Yorker. These subscriptions added to the cards, letters, books and magazines sent to me by my friends and family, led to an inordinate amount of mail being directed to one camper – namely me – which, in turn, led to my last name, SMUKLER, being yelled out by the cop over and over again at mail call.

Chief decided to make the yelling of my name a thing at the camp. He started yelling my name in the housing unit when all the campers were recalled to the unit for the 10 P.M. count. From the white neighborhoods, others joined in yelling SMUKLER. Then the calls came from the White House and pretty soon the SMUKLER war cry was ringing the unit each night as we prepared for count. A few days later, Chief asked me if I liked the chanting to which I responded that I didn't mind it but was curious as to how long this would continue. He said about six weeks and he was pretty much on target. The best was when I got a new upper bunky, a Spanish kid named OT, who his first night standing by our bunkbed waiting for the 10 P.M. count as the SMUKLER war cry goes out, turns to me and says: "Hey, who is this guy SMUKLER?" I knew I had arrived.]

Wang was a recent self-surrender who migrated to the corner of the weight room on the first day of my training where Chief was giving Murder Mike and me a tutorial on the difference between the mid, upper, and lower (ok anterior, lateral, and posterior) deltoid muscles. What motivated Wang in the weight room is what motivated so many men at the camp and, to a certain extent, motivated me – the desire to show his family that camp was making him better, healthier, stronger.

Wang had told his two boys at visit the week before that he was going to bench press 200 pounds by the time he packed out. Murder Mike, Wang and I all started the first week of January. By the time Wang packed out in April (awarded one of the pandemic get-out-of-jail golden tickets), he was benching 195 – going up 85 pounds in three months. I have no doubt he would have surpassed his goal by the end of April and gone well beyond that had he served another six months at camp. According to livestrong.com "a good goal is to bench press 1.5 times your body weight for one repetition, or 85 percent of that number for five repetitions." Let's say Wang was average height and weight for a South Korean male – 5'8" 151 pounds – his goal would have been 225 which Chief would have taken him to even if it killed him (or came close).

[Aside: Let me take a moment to share with the reader one of the most refreshing aspects of camp life – the complete and unabashed absence of political correctness. I do so here because its absence was never felt more than in the weight room.

Wang was called Wang merely because he was of Asian descent. If he was offended by the nomenclature, he did not show it. Tim was Asian Tim or Chino. Every Russian guy, and we ended up with five in the Russian car, had Russia put before his name – Russian M, Russian Gary, two Russian Alex. The word Black, not African American described everyone of that color; Spanish not Hispanic or Latino covered Mexican, Puerto Ricans, and Dominicans.

Black Lives Matter is not a thing in camp because Blacks, for the most part, control the stuff that mattered in the camp: televisions, the kitchen, the basketball court, the barber shop, the gym. Yes, Blacks bunked on the North side of the housing unit and Whites bunked on the South side. Yes, for the most part, Blacks used the sinks and toilets on the North side of the bathroom,

Whites on the South side. Yet, while the racial divide permeated all aspects of the camp, racial slurs were not tolerated. The one time the word "nigger" was used in the open by a White camper, that camper was hauled off not by the Blacks but by other Whites, and called on to apologize.

Jokes one would never hear told openly in the free world were a part of the daily life of prison camp. Yes, there was a level of misogyny that, I suspect, grows out of a womanless society but I never found the level to be so offensive as to shock. Yes, there was a sense of homophobia but, again, not beyond the pale (if a camper was talking about the size of the sausage served at lunch, he would say "No Homo" to clear it from a homophobic reference).] There was a camper gender transitioning and I never heard any derogatory comments directed "her" way. The unwritten rules that prevented the racial divides in higher security facilities from playing out in the camp, I believe, fostered the acceptance of the politically incorrect as a way of venting differences without crossing the line toward a race war.]

Two months into my weight lifting career, by early March, I was comfortable enough heading into the gym solo. As my walking routine by March 2020 dominated my schedule, I could not waver from the 2:30 gym time though sometimes Chief would need to do so to accommodate his schedule. Chief took his own car – Black White and Spanish – through the gym nightly at 7:00 P.M. with Fun Fridays becoming well known as a kind-of marine boot camp training which incorporated track work into the routine.

My comfort in the absence of Chief was limited to times in the gym when it was almost empty. I would work out on weekends when only my former bunky OT was working out (OT was a weight lifting machine and, at 5'5", I'm guessing was pound for pound the strongest in the camp).

My solo routine was a combination of machines that required no rigging of clamps or handlebars (the lateral chest machine and the back of the hamstring machine I used for biceps) then a routine that Chief taught us called "22 minutes of hell:" take two nickels, one in each hand, and do 15-minute reps of an individual swim relay – backstroke, breaststroke, butterfly, and crawl – then repeat for 22 minutes without dropping the weights to your side.

I was in a great weight lifting groove for the month of March 2020 then the pandemic hit and the first thing the BOP did was shut down the gym, wrapping crime scene tape across the door. A prison lives by the adage "necessity is the mother of invention" and never more so than when it comes to working out. Suffice to say this here: you do not need a gym membership to accomplish the exercise goals of your program. An area to walk, a hard bed or floor to do ab work, and a door knob with some exercise bands will more than fit the bill (See Part IV. Pandemic).

Chapter 24
Super Bowl Week: Hitting the
Wall Then Pushing Through

Day 232. February 2, 2020

204: 19 Pounds to Go

In late January, I was just pounds away from my original weight loss goal of 200 pounds – a drop of 85 pounds from my surrender weight and 35 pounds lower than I had ever been in the past two decades. I told my mom during a visit at the time that when I got to 200, I would reassess my plan and make the call as to whether I would push on to the 100 goal.

I had spent 24 weeks on a very regimented restrictive food program. I knew that I would be able to push past my first goal and get under 200 pounds. Looking back at this time in my journey, for the first time I became ambivalent about pressing beyond the 100-pound loss mark. I felt that I had achieved a lot; breaking 200 pounds should be enough of a weight loss statement to make to the free world; I did what I said I would do – use my time in prison as a vehicle for sustained, significant weight loss. Enough was enough.

That is not to say that I let go. Beyond a couple of anomalies which I will discuss below, the meals of January/February were not that different from the July weeks of greatest weight loss; and certainly some of the biggest drops in those early weeks could be explained away by their earliness – a drop of five pounds when you are sitting at 285 is not that much different than a drop of a single pound at 200.

But I did feel that I was loosening up on portion control: a slice of bread here, a full serving of ice cream there; a double sausage dinner here and the introduction of sliced cheese as a staple of my diet there – it was adding up over time. And the baking was taking its toll.

This is why I discount those diets that are predicated solely on intermittent fasting that make the claim that you can eat as much as you want as long as you eat it within the prescribed time windows. That was not my experience. Had I taken that advice, I may have seen results early on but I am quite sure that I would not have achieved the sustained significant weight loss over a ten-month period.

The most significant difference in my eating habits in the last week of January and first week of February was the introduction of outside meals that were not commissary-based substitutes for the inedible dinners; dinners that were not only different in types of calories consumed but in the timeline in which they were consumed. As these meals provide some insight into the culinary life of a federal prison camp, I will share them with you now.

Nell's White Clam Pizza

There are two foods that I simply cannot help but eat if presented before me: all-beef hot dogs and pizza. In dogs, give me Nathan's or Hebrew National and I can't stop. In pizza, it was Pepe's White Clam Pizza which I was introduced to back in the 90s by the Mayor of the Main Line, Drew Camerota. At the time, I was guest lecturing at the Yale Women's Campaign School. I would drive from Philly to New Haven, go straight to Pepe's, order two large white clam pizzas (which is as described: no red sauce, just cheeses, minced baby clams, and garlic – tons of garlic – in an ever-so-crisp and crunchy thin pie crust) to be picked up on my way out of town after my lecture was over later that evening.

[Note: If you decide to do this – which I highly recommend – bring large garbage bags to wrap them in before you put them into your trunk for the ride home. Failure to do so will leave a garlic smell in your car for days. Trust me on this.]

As you know, at 4:30 P.M. each day, the kitchen cop leaves, locking the kitchen up for the evening and the moveable feast – the carbopalooza – begins. Nell, a shot caller in the Spanish car, had an assistant, first Nick then Jose, run in to set up shop at the microwave table closest to the chow hall doors: stacks of commissary-bought flour tortillas, a bowl of commissary-bought tomato sauce, a large bag of shredded cheese (not commissary-bought if you get my drift), diced onions and peppers (again, not commissary-bought), and a full spice rack ready to go. On the floor by the table, a bucket of ice with commissary-bought sodas of all varieties.

Nell's Pizza kitchen was now open for business. The secret to Nell's recipe was the preparation of the pizza crust – sporking holes into the flour tortillas and nuking each side for 30 seconds thereby evaporating the water content to provide a crunchy dough upon which to build your personal pizza.

My favorite Nell's pizza was – did I give it away? – white clam. I would hand Nell a pouch of my commissary minced baby clams which he would drain, put on the prepped tortilla, add peppers, onion, garlic and cheeses then pop in the microwave. When done, add some red pepper flakes – Y Ahi Vas! – a creative culinary homage to Pepe and his New Haven institution.

Two mackerel for the pizza; one mackerel for the ice-cold diet coke and I was set.

While this was a special treat for me, for many of the guys, it was a nightly repast. Nell would get called from all sides of the chow hall/now TV room and at all times for a personal pizza. He even delivered into the housing unit and outdoors in the summer months to the White table by the Bocce court.

Murder Mike's Stromboli

While Nell's pizza operation was well into swing by the time I arrived, Murder Mike slowly emerged on the culinary scene – he arrived 18 days before me and, like me and most of the self-surrenders, needed time to feel his way.

Mike first hooked up with the Muslim car led by Sayed which acted like a co-op, pooling their commissary resources and assorted food hustles to create chicken curry or Pad Thai. Toward the end of 2019, Murder Mike decided to add his hand to the mix. Mike's coming out party was Super Bowl Sunday – an event for which he spent a full day prepping 25 strombolis for his friends – as I said, he was the nicest guy in the joint.

Mike's Stromboli, like Nell's pizza, used the commissary flour tortilla wraps as its foundation. He spent the better part of Super Bowl Sunday slicing and dicing (done usually with single edge razor blades) veggies and chicken.

For what comes next, DON'T TRY THIS AT HOME!

Once the veggies, chicken, and commissary condiments (hot pepper mix, jalapeños etc.) were stuffed and folded into the tortilla wrap, the stromboli was ready to be prepped for the microwave. It was plastic-wrapped then placed into a used potato chip bag. The chip bag would allow the stromboli tortilla to get crisp – the chemical makeup of its lining retaining the heat inside the bag while it was nuked. The metallic nature of the lining will create sparking (this I have actually seen, for you just Google "potato chip bag" + microwave) which can destroy the microwave: a disaster that could cause bodily harm if the blame for losing a microwave was laid at your bunk-step. To avoid such a calamity, the potato chip bag was placed inside a wrapping of newspapers to prevent sparking and save the microwave (or so I am told).

So the case can be made, though not a definitive one, that the weakness in my weight loss performance in weeks 25 and 26 was, in some way related to my loosening up on the reins of my diet – a loosening which simply did not happen during the course of my journey up to that point. I was not one to take a day off and splurge; I didn't have days of the week in which I ate dessert or junk food. If I had any lapse, it was ice cream-specific (a lapse that one other camper, my former bunky OT, shared as he was on as restrictive a diet as I) and even that was not an all-out spurge (at times picking out the chocolate peanut butter chunks while other times going for the whole serving). In fact, there was more than ample opportunity to ice cream cheat at camp. Each week on the bulletin board in the housing unit, CrapGame would post a list of different ice cream pints available the following week at commissary. As campers had no access to freezers (other than those who had them at their satellite work sites – or so I am told), Commissary Day (Thursday) also became ice cream day. It was not unusual to see a group of men downing whole pints of ice cream in the chow hall immediately upon returning from commissary pick up – and that was 11:30 in the morning.

Stalling out was also the result of a combination of frustration and desperation. While it took me less than 21 days to lose my first 14 pounds, it took me 99 days to lose my next 14 pounds: On November 28, 2019, my recorded weight was 213 pounds; on March 7, 2020, I weighed 199 pounds. In the last two weeks I had lost just two pounds, weighing 201 on February 21st.

Clearly, I had hit a wall.

The wall got that much higher when I was informed on March 8th that my halfway house date had finally been set for April 29th – in 51 days. I now had 51 days to drop 14 pounds if I was to meet my goal of dropping 100 pounds during my prison stay. I would now have to drop weight at a rate twice as fast as I had been dropping over the past 100 days.

Lose fourteen pounds in 51 days.

As Sean Connery said when trapped with Nicholas Cage in the cave under Wall Street in the movie National Treasure: "We must change the paradigm."

And so I did just that – changed the paradigm.

The mathematical premise of the Jailbird Diet is the same underlying most weight loss programs: a premise recognizing only two ways to change the weight loss paradigm – reduce your caloric intake and/or increase your caloric burn rate. I did both. The reduction in daily calories I will discuss a bit later in Part IV Pandemic. The caloric burn rate was simply a function of upping the number of miles I walked per day: that meant pushing my daily mile count to 12 from the 10-mile per day count I had reached in February.

To do this required a schedule adjustment. The only way to insure getting 12 miles in a day was to make sure that I completed three miles first thing in the morning, avoiding the chance that a recall would shut down the track for the entire morning thereby preventing me from making any headway on my 12. If I could take three miles in one walk session right after breakfast, I could then space out my other walks as follows: Two miles at 10:30 (just after lunch); Two miles at noon; Two miles at 1:30 (getting off the track and right over to my workout in the gym scheduled daily for 2:30, see below). With nine miles in before dinner at 3:00 P.M., I had a clear path to my 12:2 miles when count cleared generally at 5:00 P.M. Then one last mile launched after the national news broadcast ended at 7:00 P.M.

So on March 18, I stepped up my walking for the third and final time hitting the three-mile-at-a-time mark. While it took me 72 days to take the track one mile at a time, and another six months for me to jump to the next level of distance walking – two miles at a time – it took me less than a month to hit the three-mile mark.

As my stamina now allowed me to move up from one mile to three miles at a clip, my estimated time per mile was also going down from 7–8 minutes per lap or a 35–40-minute mile to a 5–6-minute lap or a 25–30-minute mile. Even with the reduction in lap times, stepping up from eight miles to ten miles to now 12 miles meant committing roughly six hours a day to the track.

Little did I know then that in ten days the BOP would cut off our access to the track leaving me to face the unthinkable: how to burn calories without spending most of my day walking.

Chapter 25
The Last Miles

Day 260. March 2, 2020

200: 15 Pounds to Go

On March 2, 2020, two things happened that changed everything for me and ended my baking career.

First, I had finally hit the 200-mark.

During my baking period, January and February, I had dropped a total of six pounds – the same amount of weight loss I had achieved the month before I started baking and nearly half of what I had lost on a monthly basis from June through November. My daily walk logs showed my time on the track had not gone down and my food logs showed, with few exceptions, a maintenance of my diet regimen. The one variable that had changed was what I was not writing down in my daily log: everything I put into my mouth while I was baking.

But now I had reached the 85-pound loss mark. It was time to fish or cut bait. So I decided to dedicate myself to the end game – reaching 185 pounds – a total of 100 pounds lost on the inside.

Second, I was informed by the Case Manager that Region had set my halfway house date for April 29.

When I was told of the Warden's approval of my halfway house application back in November, I was also told at the time that the approval would be sent to region within 48 hours and I would hear back shortly from region with a date to pack out. Once a week from December through February I went into the Case Manager's office to inquire about the status of my paperwork. Every week for four months I was told the same thing: your paperwork is still in Records.

[Aside: Everything in the BOP is a mystery surrounded by a bureaucracy which, I suspect, happens for a reason. If you wanted to file a complaint, you would fill out a form called a BP8 and hand it to Counselor West. If that form was not responded to in writing in five business days, you could then fill out a request for a BP9 which had to be signed by Counselor West at which time you could then file the actual BP9. If the BP9 was not responded to in a timely fashion, you could repeat the process and file a BP10. There was also a form called a Sensitive 10 which you could file without notifying Counselor West (or so I am told).

Records, the office that was holding my paperwork and not sending it to region (they were also holding 14 other campers' paperwork at the same time), was situated just across the service road in the Medium Security prison. To hear the Case Manager and his secretary talk about the Records office, you would think it was someplace in, let's say, Texas.

Texas. Where the most mysterious of all places in the BOP exists, a place called Grand Prairie.

To hear inmates speak of Grand Prairie, you would think you were in the Land of Oz and they were talking about the Emerald City. Grand Prairie is where the Wizard lived: the little man who was the final arbiter of all complaints raised by any prisoner across the BOP; the little man who had the final say on designating your out time; the little man who, peaking through the castle wall, would more often than not tell you to go away.

This is how the BOP describes Gran Prairie:

"The Grand Prairie Office Complex, located in Grand Prairie, Texas, was created to better serve employees and consolidate various processes to achieve more streamlined, efficient, and cost-effective Bureau-wide operations. It contains three components, each specializing in a unique subject:

- the Human Resource Services Center
- the Designations and Sentence Computation Center,
- the Field Acquisition Office.

This Office Complex includes more than 500 employees with expertise in human resources; inmate classification, designations, and sentence calculation; and financial management."

I would regularly hear of prisoners talking about a contact they had at Grand Prairie. While I never had to go to the DefCon 4 of prison complaints that would make it to Grand Prairie, I was keenly interested in my halfway house date. Not because I was that interested in leaving camp for the halfway house as, from all the stories I had heard about the Philly halfway houses, they were no picnic. But halfway could, just maybe, provide me an opportunity that camp could not provide: the potential weekend furlough that would allow me to see two of my daughters graduate – both would be graduating that May in Massachusetts, beyond the 100-mile radius for any furlough I could get from camp.]

Finally, in mid-February I was told that my paperwork had left Records for Region; ten days later I was given my halfway house date – April 29. I had 15 pounds to go and 60 days to get there. So I untied my baker's apron, resigned from the kitchen entirely, strapped on my LeBron's, and never looked back.

With the freed-up time, I moved my daily walking from 6 miles to ten miles to 12 miles. This meant devoting nearly six hours a day to walking with another hour spent in the gym. My weekly weight loss was tracking up as well hitting two pounds lost in each of the last two weeks. I was on a clear glide path to 185.

Then the pandemic hit.

Part IV
Pandemic

Chapter 26
Lock Down

Day 289. March 31, 2020

195: 10 Pounds to Go

"I have paid no poll-tax for six years. I was put into jail once on this account, for one night; and as I stood considering the walls of solid stone, two or three feet thick, the door of wood and iron, a foot thick, and the iron grating which strained the light, I could not help being struck with the foolishness of that institution which treated me as if I were mere flesh and blood and bones, to be locked up."

Civil Disobedience, p. 10

By the end of February, we knew something was going to happen. Then, in the second week of March, all visits were cancelled – a measure the BOP attempted to make easier to deal with, in part, by giving us more time on the phone. Then the crime tape went up across the entrance to the weight room and we realized our world too was about to change. The curious thing about the BOP is that its one-rule-fits-all-institutions approach can lead to some inane results and, when that happens, the BOP doesn't seem to care.

The BOP response to Covid-19 was to lockdown all institutions. This may make sense for institutions in which prisoners are housed in separate cells or rooms – contain the virus by keeping prisoners in two- or four-man cells thereby limiting the opportunity to spread the virus to the entire population. It may even make sense to buttress this social distancing by expanding chow hours to allow prisoners to social distance while eating; or regulate shower times to allow social distancing in the bathroom.

But locking down a camp – where lockdown means forbidding campers from ever going outside – is nuts; it actually enforces the opposite of social distancing as it requires 120 campers to stay in a housing unit where (1) bunkbeds are never more than 16 inches away from the next camper (2) eating occurs in a chow hall where no diner is ever more than 6 inches from the next camper and (3) a shower, shit, and shave is never more than a few feet from another camper in the bathroom. A lockdown at a camp prevents prisoners from going to the one place in the camp where they *can* social distance – outside.

The pandemic had a weird effect on the camp. On the television monitors we could see the free world changing – the evacuation of city streets, the wearing of masks, the inundation of emergency rooms etc. – but our world remained eerily the same. The only impact the pandemic had on the inside was the posting of fliers discussing social distancing (go figure) and hygiene – the cops shaving off their facial hair and wearing masks, and commissary being brought down from the warehouse to be distributed in the chow hall.

The greatest impact remained our confinement indoors which, for me, created a bit of a crisis in my weight loss program. As I was up to 12 miles per day walking and now had 11 pounds to lose in 45 days, closing off the track was a real blow to my goal and the rather tight timetable I had to reach it.

I replaced walking with an aggressive ab/leg workout. I would do three sets of fifty sit-ups, frog kicks (get on your back with legs raised and bent at 45-degree angle then do a frog leg kick fifty times), then leg lifts (on your side, legs extended lift straight leg vertical 50 times then switch legs for another 50).

This new regimen was made easier because of the pandemic's easing of the privacy rules in the housing unit. The acceptance of sheets and towels hanging down from the top bunks to create privacy for the lower bunks was now extended beyond the 4:00 P.M. to 7:30 A.M. timetable. As we were now stuck inside with each other 24/7, the cops realized that bowing to our privacy demands would be a good thing for all concerned. Good fences do indeed make good neighbors. So my "I Dream of Genie" set up was now a permanent arrangement allowing me to work out on my bed with some degree of privacy.

I recorded these workouts with Professor Mead as I recorded laps around the track. At the end of the day, I completed 10 sets of 50. Doing 500 of any exercises I am sure burns calories; how many calories, I do not know. I was pretty sure I was not burning as many calories as I was going around the track 60 times a day, but it was still something.

What I did not lose out on was my weight room workout; it just was no longer in the weight room and was no longer pushing weights.

There is no more creative group of men on the planet than a group of inmates faced with the shutdown of their weight room. The hallway leading from the housing unit to the chow hall became the impromptu workout area. Within days of the weight room shut down, and seemingly out of nowhere, weight bands of all colors, widths and lengths began to show up in the hallway. Chief began leading cars on a schedule that stretched from 7:00 A.M. through the evening. My car secured the 7:00 P.M. slot at which time we assembled by the double doors at the end of the hallway leading to the outside for our session.

Bands were strung up from the sprinkler pipe, or wrapped around the metal partition of the double door, or strapped under a chair, or placed under our feet; each placement replicating a machine or free weight exercise we would do in the gym. Most of the guys walked away from these workouts believing they had done more for their muscles with the bands than with the iron bars or discs. I had to agree: my toughest workouts were in the hallway using bands.

Still, I was under the gun, so to speak, when it came to my weight loss timetable. If I could get to three pounds dropped a week, I would just make goal by the 29th of April. So I changed the paradigm – dropping my food intake to force the calories down. I skipped most lunches, hustling my protein over to Chief, and moving into the diet I thought I was going to maintain when I came in: mackerel and mayo or clams and cheese became my staple proteins and fats at mealtime; I stopped bananas and any other fruit with the exception of apples (if they were good which was rare). I killed the Gracey Goodies but kept the M&Ms and oatmeal packet pinches. In short, I was as hardcore on caloric intake as I was in the earliest weeks when I was dropping 3–5 pounds every seven days.

Then the Lord intervened on April 9, 2020 – the first day of Passover. As I have told you, the BOP bends over backward to recognize religious tradition, particularly when it comes to food. The Russian car, now filled with five practicing Jews, along with Big Jew (an orthodox rabbi) and Half-Jew (the inmate who requests Kosher food at meals then scarfs down a pepperoni and cheeses pizza at carbo-palooza) led the Passover parade making sure that even those of us in the car who did not feel HaShem like they did, at least ate like they did.

Passover for the Jewish car meant foregoing the chow hall for meals taken or picked up in the room in the trailer known as the Chapel.

So each morning at 8:00 the Russian car would take the day's Passover meals to the Chapel for pick up. The daily haul consisted of the following: breakfast – a cheese omelet; lunch – a Swanson Hungry Man Meal like kosher meal of fish, chicken, or beef all with a starch, and container of matzoh ball soup; dinner – matzoh, tuna fish, and cheese. There were apples and plums (a rarity) throughout the week as well as grape juice and matzoh to your hearts content.

The highlights for me were the omelet and tuna fish. I gave away my lunch protein to Chief or my neighbor RR substituting in my mackerel and mayo or, at times, just peanut butter on matzoh. The forced caloric restriction of seven days of Passover without eating the Hungry Mensch dinner allowed me to hit the three pounds lost in each of the last two weeks before I packed out on the 16th of April.

Passover played another critical role in the end game of my camp diet.

We continued on lockdown which meant that we remained locked inside with no access to the track. The absurdity of our situation did not go unnoticed by some of the cops who would allow us to go onto the wooden deck off the back of the housing unit which stretched between the dorm and the weight room. As lockdown went beyond one week, we were also allowed to go to the laundry room which was in the farthest room down the trailer that lined the far side of the basketball court. And because it was Passover, the Jews were allowed to go to the Chapel pretty much any time during the week – two doors closer in from the laundry down the trailer.

These housekeeping and religious dispensations allowed me to devise a hybrid walking circuit – under the guise of walking to the laundry or chapel which now was not considered out-of-bounds – that ran from the back door of the housing unit, crossed the outdoor wooden deck, proceeded up the concrete ramp to the trailer, then left down to the chapel then down to the laundry room, then turn around and head back to the outdoor deck and the door to the housing unit. I calculated my distance not by laps but by time – every 25 minutes, a mile was logged with Professor Mead.

As I have said, the pandemic, while it locked us inside, did not change much of our daily existence. The cops passed out masks on the tenth day of the lockdown with no directions as to when or where they should be worn. Maybe 20% of the men began wearing them; within 48 hours all but a handful ever put them on. But beyond that, and the big jars of hand sanitizer on the cop station, little had changed on the inside since the onset of the pandemic. We had access to the chow hall with the same meal and television schedule. Workouts were taking place in the hallway. And the cops were loosening up on the outdoor prohibition allowing us to sit on the deck and, for me, do my hybrid laps.

I was now in a pretty good place. At the beginning of Passover, I had 20 days till my out date with 10 pounds to go. It was going to be close; I was going to really have to push, but I now had my walking back in gear, a daily band workout in the hallway, an ab/leg workout and a drive-to-the-finish-line eating mentality; I thought I could make it.

Then something happened in the camp that had never happened before. Word began to spread of lists being drawn up in the Case Manager's office; lists of men who were going to have their sentences shortened; men who were going to be sent home early because of the pandemic. Rumors had been flying ever since the visits were shut down in March that the BOP was going to move prisoners' home. The old white car became even more obsessed with their out-date calculations figuring if anyone was going home it would be them. Some in the car would be downright gleeful upon hearing the news that prisoners in other BOP facilities had succumbed to the virus in the hopes that more deaths would spur the BOP to quicker action and earlier release dates.

For most prisoners, this was a dream they had been dying to hear every day for years. It meant your transition from the world of incarceration to the world of the free is finally about to begin; the dreamed-for day that you can leave the camp and the cops behind. Prisoners were contacting lawyers on the outside and consulting with those on the inside as to the provisions of the emergency pandemic legislation that broadened the scope of compassionate release.

BP8s and 9s were flying demanding compassionate release.

Then on April 8, Rocap, the Case Manager, came into the housing unit. This, in and of itself, while not a common occurrence was not that unusual; occasionally Rocap would come to the cop station and do a count. But this time was most unusual because in his hand he was carrying a list and on that list were the names of campers who were going to go home before their time had come.

It is hard to imagine just how bizarre this moment is for a camper; particularly one who has been incarcerated for more than a few years. Every day of those years is a day closer to the day that a case manager tells you your out date – the day you will be leaving incarceration for a halfway house, home confinement, or probation. You don't even get to that day – the day you are told your out date – until ten to twelve months from your out date. So for years you sit waiting for the moment at which an outdate has been officially assigned to you; it is then that you can begin to get your mind around going home.

Prior to the pandemic, Rocap would always call a camper into his office and give him the news privately. Then the news would spread throughout the camp like wild fire that so-and-so got his out date. Never, and I mean never, were out dates given en masse. And now, here stood Rocap with the list and everybody gathered round the cop station (which meant on top of my bed) to hear the news. Expectations had been running high, particularly among the over-65-with-underlying-medical-conditions-crowd that they would be on the list. Pandemics play winners and losers and the conventional wisdom on the inside was that the losers in the free world – the more elderly and infirm – were the winners in the BOP world most likely on the list of the first to be packed out.

Then Rocap reads the list and the conventional wisdom is proven wrong. Of the eighteen campers on the list, less than a handful fit the elderly-with-pre-existing-medical-condition universe. The list was comprised primarily of the most senior members – the shot callers – of the Black, Spanish, and Asian cars. H, with 16 years down and 4 to go. Juice with 23 down and 5 to go. Chino with 12 down and three to go. All made the list. None had medical conditions. Yes, there were a few from the old White car but this list was not what we all thought it was going to be. Rocap professed disbelief explaining that the call had been made by the Region and not his office. There would be other lists he assured the men.

The room was stunned. Cheering, hugging, and cries of joy broke out all over the housing unit. Men ran to the phones and computers to tell their family and friends.

Of all the stupid and non-sensical decisions the BOP had made in the short time I was under their supervision – and there were plenty – its approach to identifying which prisoners would first leave Fairton was not one of them. In fact, it was wise beyond belief. Here's why.

Had the first eighteen prisoners to be released from the camp by the pandemic followed the conventional wisdom of being based entirely upon age and medical condition, the overwhelming majority on the list would have been from the White car. Such a move would have been the closest thing to triggering a riot in the camp as I could imagine. As I have told you, race divides prisoners in camps just as it divides neighborhoods in the free world. But in camps, there is a trigger point at which the racial divide transforms from an unfortunate necessary evil to becoming a dangerous climate for tension and perhaps retribution. In a few months, the world would see this inflection point play out in the free world in the wake of George Floyd's murder. In prison, it takes a lot less than the video choke hold murder of a Black man by a White cop for this inflection to point to be reached – and the BOP knows it.

Releasing the shot callers of the Black, Spanish, and Asian cars first allowed the BOP to subsequently release those whose health and life were most at risk in a prison during a pandemic – release the old White guys – without creating a firestorm of unrest in the camp.

I was White and old when I served my time but thankfully exhibited none of the underlying medical conditions warranting early release. If morbid obesity was such a condition, I had removed it from my medical chart over the past ten months.

I was not on the first list nor, I was told by Rocap, would I be on any subsequent list. The reason being that in March I had already been given my out date of April 29th. Prisoners that already had out dates would be processed outside of this new pandemic move-out schedule as though the pandemic did not happen. This was great news, I thought, because hearing your name called on the lists did have one significant downside – you had to go into solitary confinement in the Medium for 14 days before you could be released home. This move to solitary was mandated by one of Attorney General Barr's flurry of pandemic memos, the upside of which was moving us directly to home confinement in many cases years before our out dates, the downside being two weeks of solitary confinement in the Medium.

If you have not figured out by now, I was one of the luckiest of the lucky in the federal prison system. I was going to serve less than a year – what Le Carre would call "less time than it takes to get the McDonalds and pussy stink off you." I would spend my time in a park-like setting free to read, write, puzzle, and walk to my heart's content. While the all-in-one-dormitory experience may sound dreadful, I slept more peacefully at night over the past ten months than I had in the last three years. I was, for the most part, left to myself but enjoyed the times I did interact with my fellow prisoners. I had become far more fit and healthier than I had been at any point in my life.

Isolation would put a crimp in my prison lifestyle to say the least. We were told that isolation meant one-man-one-cell and zero outdoor activity. Pretty grim compared to what I was used to. Even more grim as I was still behind the weight loss curve when it came to reaching goal: On March 31 I logged in at 195; on April15, I was at 192 – 7 pounds from goal. At this rate, I would only make it to 189, 4 pounds from goal. While I could kick up my calorie burn in the camp by pushing my walk schedule (though that was not a given as Passover was ending and my sham walk to the Chapel would no longer give me cover for my newly designed track), the calorie burn in isolation would be limited to what I could do in a cell; not much to my thinking.

I had made it off the first list which Rocap called out in the housing unit. Then I missed the list that he called out in the chow hall; a moment I will never forget. If you ever want to know what "cutting the tension with a knife" means, imagine sitting in a room full of prisoners – some with as much a five to ten years left on their sentences – when a list is being read out of those who would get to go home in two weeks. A list that would truly change the course of their lives forever.

It was the morning of April 16, 2020. One more day without being called over to the Medium for isolation and I figured I was home free – as quarantine was a 14-day affair and my out date of the 29th would be less than 14 days away. Then I heard the three words I dreaded most:

"Smukler. Pack Out!"

Chapter 27
Big Boy Prison

Day 266. April 16, 2020

192: 7 Pounds to Go

"I should not talk so much about myself if there were nobody else whom I knew as well. Unfortunately, I am confined to this theme by the narrowness of my experience."

Henry David Thoreau Walden p. 3

A butterfly flaps its wings off the coast of Australia and a Cat-5 hurricane slams into the Big Easy.

A Chinaman sets up a bat tartar concession stand at an open-air market in Wuhan (if you thought a book on weight loss from a prisoner's perspective would cow-tow to political correctness, think again) and I am sitting locked down 24/7 in Delta Wing Left 215 – a 7' × 9' cinderblock cell in a medium security federal prison with an Uzbeki-born Jew from Long Island sharing a toilet and taking our meals and temperature through the slot in the door for the next fourteen days.

The Butterfly Effect? Chaos Theory? Or Karma which Shantaram, in the eponymous novel, warns is a hammer, not a feather.

It's just me and G, a toilet, a locker, a desk, two plastic chairs, and a bunk bed. And it will be this way for the next 14 days other than the four times we are allowed to walk to the shower which, just our luck, is not a walk at all as it is right next to our cell.

I am writing in the early morning hours. My window to the world – a 15" × 36" wide slit with two bars running vertically through it. I look out on a razor wire fence that travels west the length of the prison yard to the administrative building 500 yards on the other side. I can see the parking lot that separates the medium security prison from the camp I called home for the past ten months. Though I can't see the camp, I can see the top of the tree line that separated the camp from the free world.

I place my plastic chair to face the window. My celly (always found it somewhat humorous that even the toughest of inmates would refer to their bunkmate as bunky and cellmate as celly – names more suited to characters in nursery rhymes than to incarcerated criminals)…my celly, G doesn't sleep well at night; he tries to watch television but that requires propping up both chairs, craning your neck, and pressing your forehead to the window slit in the cell door – all in an attempt to see the 36" television screen perched 100 feet on the other side of common room around which the cells of the triangular Delta wing are situated. When not by the door, he is drawing at the table or tossing above me in his bed. But now he sleeps.

And there is quiet. Before the inmates of Delta wing attempt cell-to-cell communication across the common indoor area that separates us; before the banging on the metal shower door for a bar of soap; before the gangsta rapper in the next cell over begins his impromptu concert; before dusk falls and the inmates begin the cacophony of jungle sounds that makes you feel like you are in a rain forest. Before all of that, I write.

Each morning for the next 13 days, I will spend looking through my window over the razor wire and beyond to the beige metallic A-frame buildings with their dark green roofs across the yard, beyond the parking lot that separates this Medium Security facility from the camp to the top of the tree line to the west; the pines and oaks that greeted me each morning of my 310 days at the federal prison known as Fairton FCI Satellite Camp – the place where I lost 100 pounds and found myself.

The following are excerpts from the logs dated April 16 through April 29, 2020 – my last days of confinement spent in the Medium.

4.17 First full day of isolation.

Having been told at R&D [where I passed through to enter isolation] that we would be provided underwear, T-shirts, socks, today, Friday, told no clothing until Monday…means I go three days in same underwear…still no mattress with pillow [the BOP provides each inmate a standard-issue mattress with a built-in pillow; the mattress I was given had the pillow cut out of it leaving me with a 5' mattress – I am over 6' – and no pillow]...no full blanket [the blanket I was given also was torn off at the end]...have asked for Bible (afraid I will run out of reading material)...just took temperature as they did yesterday through the slot in the door...breakfast same as bags in camp...no bowl, spoon, or cup yet.

6:04 P.M. Banging from both showers now screaming from one shower right next to our cell in corner...no cops in sight, yelling from different cells...guys now banging on cell doors from all sides last two hours...had the chaplain bring me a Bible – goal: read entire Old and New Testament...got through Genesis and 1/2 of Exodus.

4.18 Day 3 of Isolation

Fear will run out of paper, pen...cloudy day reinforces gloom in cell...last night froze in bed...figured out way to scrunch up [and] pull blanket [from] feet to top of head to breathe warm air [underneath]...place hands between thighs to keep warm...using sweatpants for pillow so legs uncovered.

12:03 P.M. first yelling of the day...G cut a deck of cards out of matzoh box [he brought in with him]...played Russian card game (2 clubs/10 diamonds) and Black Jack...I played house.

4.19. Day 4 of Isolation

Again froze last night in bed...three nights in a row of bologna sandwiches (tonight no cheese)...yelling died down today...told we get phone call tomorrow...read *Old Testament* last two days, just started New...yelling, banging now picking up.

4.20. Day 5 of Isolation

Nights are bad...freezing temperatures continue with one threadbare blanket and equally ratty sheets...as we are closest to shower, go first at 6:20 A.M....just received shirt, underwear, socks...asked for new towel – denied...told we'll get cell phone call today...we'll see...no family commun[ication] for four days during pandemic (for those in lockdown through no fault of their own) is CRUEL!

Food is slop – bologna sandwiches three nights running...today bean slush, peas, cornbread for lunch...told they have phones in place but no schedule – maybe tomorrow...we r housed in craziness...one doing bird calls now.

4.21 Day 6 of Isolation

Woke up 7:05 to take temperature 97.2…told health care services that we were more likely to die in here of pneumonia than from Covid…he said he is not HVAC…typical BOP…pray we get phone today…afraid G is gonna lose it if he can't talk to his wife…yesterday told that two portable phones were set up but call schedule not worked out – again typical BOP (Broke On Purpose)…bird calling started at 12:36 again…earlier yelling about the sanitization of the phones (lack thereof)…phones now being carted cell to cell…looks like we'll be able to call this afternoon…fingers crossed…crushing newspapers to place as stuffing inside shirt for pillow…just spoke to Shelly…1/2way house has not been told that I am going directly to home confinement…typical BOP cluster fuck.

We get CO Price from camp [Price was the first cop I came into contact with at the camp – the cop who looked at me like I was crazy when I asked him if there was someplace I needed to go after my first 4:00 P.M. count, *see Chapter 2, Shock and Awful*] who comes off as a hard ass but always OK by me…he sees me thru window and says, "Hey Smukler"…and within minutes finally have real mattress…speaks to the mercurial nature of BOP – after five days and ten COs finally got one who was decent enough to deliver.

4.22 Day 7 of Isolation

Temp 97.2. First time I have walked! Went downstairs, crossed commons to get new shirt, underwear, towel…showered…seems like the BOP got the memo…after six days with one shirt, one brief, one socks they now give us three shorts, two briefs, three socks laundry bag, pair of khakis…G cuts his into shorts, I will stay in sweats.

Bologna again for dinner means BOP batting four for seven nights bologna.

4.23 Day 8 of Isolation

The first banana arrives in breakfast bag – it's been fruit cup for past days [none of which I ate as it is pure sugar] today spaghetti with chicken and greens for lunch.

Here's what I mean by asshole. Two cops bring around book cart. G takes two thru slot to look at, they tell him to return one and stand in front of the cart to block my view while he is choosing…when I tell him [the cop] I can't see the cart, he tells me to check my glasses…I tell him: what do you think we're trying to steal books in here…first time in > 300 days I said anything to a cop that sounded at all defiant…24/7 confinement does that to you, I guess.

They distribute commissary sheet – only food on it was Snickers Bars and potato chips – I didn't fill it out…coordinated banging on doors as CO hands out food (5:05)…dunno why.

4.24 Day 9 of Isolation

Restless night, ankle pain right side of heel. Newspaper pillow needs refill…second walk (if you could call it that) to far side of unit for shower…Wang in next [shower stall – there were two on either side of Delta Wing Left] told [him] who was on the 28th list [Wang and his group left before the third pandemic list of campers getting out of jail was revealed so he had not heard who was on the list]…saw Boog, Juice H in triple corner…told them all [who was on list] as well.

The last two nights I have had food dreams…last night I was getting a soft pretzel with sesame (looked like the Dunkin Donut sesame bagel dough twisted, then spiral carved ham w/Dijon mustard)

Daily routine: temp 7:00 A.M., B [breakfast] write till 10:00 exercise/puzzle/ex/read/ex [exercise]/L [lunch] puzzle/ex [exercise]/read/puzzle/ex/read NAP at 2–4 count ex D [dinner] ex/puzzle/read/ex/puzzle/read cards [the Russian card game which I call two clubs-ten diamonds] ex/puzzle/read/ex/puzzle/read BED 10:30.

No bowel movement for 4–5 days…assume due to very limited intake – can only guess weight loss but pretty sure dropping…energy waning which I think has me napping for the first time since went down.

4.25 Day 10 of Isolation

Temp 97.0…cold again last night…again food dream – Handel's [our go-to ice cream place back home] butter pecan…lunch discarded (meatloaf)…subbed almond butter.

4.26. Day 11 of Isolation

Quietest day since I've been locked in here…lord works in mysterious ways…still freeze at night…[my] temp up in mid 97s now (97.6/97.2)…been writing almost all day…remember Sasha Issenberg [a friend] would go on a tramp steamer to write his books – no internet/no nothing…beginning to understand why…been crashing on diet as hard as possible…really miss my Detecto in the A.M.…bologna again for dinner – to think, my favorite WaWa hoagie was bologna/provolone/mayo/onion – now don't ever wanna see bologna again…G schooled me on a NY bagel called The Oligarch…everything [bagel], lox, cream cheese, onion, eggs YUM!

Tonight 7:38 jungle sounds start up from all sides the unit…monkeys, birds, lions…spooky – kinda cool.

4.27. This date of log is missing.

4.28. Day 13 of Isolation

They just took George, Monkey, and I think H out…watched them as they crossed courtyard to the outer fence…good news/bad news…good is H leaving (down for 16 with 4 to go) he came in [to isolation] two days before me…bad news, frosty/monkey kept in isolation > 18 days…G pacing between door and window – had hopes of leaving today now seem dashed. To top it off, only milk given for breakfast.

9:30 now seeing 20 guards running to "A" building…now coming out.

Bowel movement this A.M.

Typical BOP now told Shelly came to pick me up yesterday – UGH – also told I will be released tomorrow – that's the good; the bad – G just told he would now be released next Tuesday, May 5 – a week from today – [he is] miserable.

And that was it. Two weeks of Big Boy Prison.

My takeaways from two-weeks in isolation:

First, two weeks in a cell with little to no opportunity to walk let alone walk outside in fresh air can start playing with your mind. I cannot imagine what months living under such conditions would do to me. I have big respect for anyone who makes it through short-term isolation able to function in the free world without succumbing to a deep seeded resentment toward God country, and the BOP.

Second, even in the short amount of time I was kept in isolation, I felt my body growing weaker. Yes, I was doing 500 of everything each day, and adding 250 sissy pushups (push-ups onto the arms of a chair) daily to the routine, but there is something about the lack of fresh air and the close quarters that was taking its toll on me.

Third, if you think prison is a great place to reduce caloric intake (which as we have seen it may or may not be), isolation can kick the caloric reduction into high gear insuring weight loss at a very speedy clip. While my greatest weekly weight loss hit 5 pounds in weeks 5, 6, and 7, I was walking a minimum of three miles a day or 21 miles a week to achieve those numbers. In my last two weeks, I was hitting the top of my weight loss spectrum yet walking zero miles; the weight loss burden being almost entirely carried through a severely restricted diet. No wonder I started dreaming about food for the first time during my entire incarceration while in isolation.

While I pretty much maintained my caloric intake for breakfast consuming cereal and milk every day in isolation, I drastically reduced all other calories during the day. For lunch, there was very little protein that could be extracted from the starches, so I saved my apple or banana (on days we got fresh fruit in the breakfast bag) then stocked the peanut butter we got during some of the dinners to eat on G's matzoh. For dinner, it was bologna, and bologna, and bologna. There were no cheats – no peanut M&Ms, no Gracey's Goodies butterscotch, no government cheese, and no maple walnut oatmeal packs.

Pegging calorie counts now to my meals during the fourteen days I was in isolation, my calorie count most likely ranged between 750 and 1200 calories per day; pretty much starving myself in a cell. The result was dramatic. I went into isolation weighing 192 pounds. I came out after 14 days weighing 185 pounds; a loss of 7 pounds in 14 days.

Do not try this part of my diet at home. I only engaged in it by being forced by the circumstance of isolation and a mindset that was prepared to use the direness of my setting to achieve an overarching goal. Such dieting left me feeling washed out and frail after two weeks. I was in a state of constant chill for the first ten days of home confinement and felt much older than I had felt going into isolation just fourteen days before. It took me almost two weeks in home confinement to take the chill out of me and start feeling stronger again.

Epilogue

Day 308. April 29, 2020
Weight: Unknown. Pounds to Go: Unknown

6:15 A.M. This will be my last log entry from camp.

At 6:00 A.M. each morning the loud speakers welcome the men trapped within these walls to a new day. It is hard to make out the message as it bounces off the steel and concrete; something like the TSA announcements at the airport. "Report any suspicious activity." "Do not leave any bags unattended."

Baggage. Stuffed full of the hopes, dreams, memories, failures, successes, frustrations, weaknesses, hate, pain, love, and loss. All bunched up, thrown together, locked in and shut tight. Thrown together in a hurry as if there was a sudden change of plans – a plane to catch, a bus ride to take, a train pulling out of the station.

Baggage. Assigned and stamped with a number and a barcode – 76315-066.

Baggage. Placed on the scale before being thrown down onto the belt.

Baggage. Traveling along the belt toward the hole in the wall; the wall that finally separates it from wife, children, brothers and sisters, mothers, fathers, aunts, uncles...and friends. Thrown through the hole in the wall by a man wearing a black shirt with the last words you will see in the free world emblazoned on it:

We Face What You Fear.

Darkness. A new world.

Lifted, dropped, bounced, kicked. Moving upward, downward, sideways. No control. Upward, downward, sideways. No control. Traveling slower, then faster, then stopping. No control. Waiting. Waiting. Waiting. Then moving once again. Upward. Downward. Sideways. No control.

I crash. I soar.

CrapGame's mom dies of terminal cancer. A beautiful woman. I had seen her on visits. He was not allowed to attend the funeral. Neither was his father or brother, both locked up in other prisons. I imagine her being buried alone. I am 76315-066 and I crash.

Nell takes a wet rag and helps J. wash his body because J. cannot wash himself. J is in a wheelchair having lost the use of all his limbs save his left arm when an errant bullet crashed into the back of his skull during a drug deal gone bad. Nell tenderly washes J. as he sits in his wheelchair by his bed. I am 76315-066 and I soar.

Chief comes in from the phone room and screams across the unit, "I hate my life!" His son has just told him that he is afraid he will not see him until after he gets out of college. The son is 16. I am 76315-066 and I crash.

Tabby and the Black Car spend an entire weekend preparing a holiday meal, cutting veggies with single edge blades, pasting tortillas together to make pizza crust, pooling peanut butter jars from the commissary to make chocolate peanut butter layer cake. We are celebrating a camper's release – he had been down for 19 years – and all campers – Black, White, Spanish, Chinese, Muslim and this Jew – are invited to join in the celebration. I am 76315-066 and I soar.

Acorn finds out that his eighteen-year-old son has been shot dead by a cop in Baltimore. Acorn is 35. I am 76315-066 and I crash.

The case manager comes into the housing unit with a list – the get-out-of-jail-free cards – those whose sentences will be cut short to be sent home rather than stay incarcerated during a pandemic. Juice and H are both on the list. Juice has been down for 23 years with 3 more to go. H down for 16 with four to go. Neither has an underlying medical condition. Neither is over 65. They are going home. I am 76315-066 and I soar.

P2 has been complaining of gastro-intestinal pain since he got here. It gets so bad that he hands me a plastic bag filled with tissues of blood from his stool to hand to the cop just before he falls out in the bathroom. This is the second time he has faked an emergency to get medical attention outside of the prison walls. The cops don't buy it. The next day he is given four shots for faking it. A week later he is finally taken out of the prison at 3:00 A.M. to go down the road for tests. He has cancer of the rectum. He has just months left on his five-year sentence. He comes back to the bunk muttering, "I must have done something really bad to deserve this." In five days he is packed out to go to Butner – the federal prison medical facility in North Carolina – to begin six

199

weeks of chemo, and if successful, prepare for surgery. I am 76315-066 and I crash.

P2 in the week he is to start chemo fakes a fall in the bathroom not for himself but to protect Acorn who is over the fence line when a surprise count is called. The fake fall out pulls the cop into the bathroom delaying the count for ten minutes. When the count proceeds, Acorn is at his bed. I am 76315-066 and I soar.

Russian Matt, my neighbor, is not on any list. He came to the camp from the federal medical facility in Butner with a medical condition (I don't know what) that puts him in pill line and makes him lethargic for most of the day The other four Russians – his buddies – are all now going home. I am 76315-066 and I crash.

Milo, AC, Cheddar, and the Big I sit in their heavy green jackets bracing against the January cold as the sun sets on the picnic bench in the far end of Central Park – an informal meeting of those trapped in their former lives by addiction. They hold hands and read Scripture each pushing the other to find their better, kinder, stronger souls. I am 76315-066 and I soar.

And now I am moving forward, forward, forward. The upward, downward, sideways is behind me. The waiting, waiting, waiting is behind me. And there is the wall. There is the opening I travelled through ten months ago. And I am through it. I fall down to the carousel and move to my left. And the carousel stops. A new waiting begins.

What's that? A soft tap on the shoulder. I haven't felt a human touch for all my incarcerated days. I turn to see their faces...those who have kept my memories for me on the outside...my memories – the loves, hates, fears, and hopes – every one of those 310 days. They hug me tightly as if to tell my handlers: "These memories are his not yours; these memories are ours, not yours. They were always ours; they were never yours."

I raise my hand. It has my number clenched between its fingers.

185.

I will not let it go.

I cannot let it go.

I am 76315-066.

And I am.

Finally.

Home.

Notes

Shock and Awful

What sensory assault does to one's appetite and, therefore, one's ability to achieve significant sustained weight loss is an area beyond my understanding; that sensory assault, the type of which I underwent in the first days and months of my incarceration, created the platform upon which I could launch a significant, sustained weight loss program is, for me, undeniable.

The closest I can come to some scientific underpinning for this relationship between sensory assault and eating is the relationship in children of something called Sensory Process Disorder (SPD) and eating disorders. I offer up the following primer on the subject: while certainly not meant to explain how Shock and Awful triggered my weight loss program, the aspects of SPD and the manifestations of the eating disorder discussed below, present eerily similar aspects of my body's reaction to Shock and Awful and, as you have seen in the chapter on food, the new type of eating patterns I engaged in.

Sensory Process Disorder (SPD), formerly known as Sensory Integration Dysfunction, occurs when the brain has difficulty processing information through the senses [1].

It is a spectrum, affecting one or more of the senses and usually with a combination of sensitivities. It can affect up to 16 percent of school-aged children in the United States.

SPD is typically common in those who have autism and attention deficit hyperactivity disorder [2]. Many children who struggle with SPD are sensitive to things such as tags on the inside of a shirt, the sound of a vacuum, or might be uncoordinated. Many are picky eaters and orally defensive when dealing with taste, smell, sound and texture of foods.

Eating Disorders can come from a combination of behavioral, biological, emotional, psychological, interpersonal, and social factors. They can create a cycle of physical and emotional destruction.

How SPD Relates to Eating Disorders

Eating fewer than ten foods and significantly struggling to try new foods is beyond picky eating and a concern that an eating disorder might be emerging.

In children with SPD, some may be obese, underweight or even normal weight, but all seem to suffer from nutritional deficiencies due to limited food choices. According to Dr. Kay Tomboy of SOS Feeding Solutions in Denver, eating is the most complicated human behavior and involves all areas of human development. She goes on to report that research shows from birth to age 8, 20 percent of all children struggle with *feeding challenges* [3].

Eating a meal is a complex sensory experience consisting of foods with ranging appearance, odors, textures, and tastes, as well as other individuals who contribute to conversation and hearing senses during meal time. Motor planning is also used for postural control and manipulation of utensils when eating.

An association between feeding issues and SPD suggests that they are picky eaters, rarely eat the same meal as the rest of family, do not want foods to touch and may have aversions to tastes, textures and refusal of food due to odors. These are similar traits found in those with eating disorders or Avoidant Restrictive Food Intake Disorder (ARFID) [4].

When an individual's ability to tolerate specific foods is *affected*, SPD can produce symptoms similar to eating disorders. Situations such as long, drawn-out meal times and small appetite can lead to poor nutrition and significant weight loss [5].

A severe dislike of foods due to texture, odor, or taste can occur as the brain struggles to incorporate sensory messages regarding taste, sight, smells of foods. Lack of sensory regulation may emerge as avoidance around certain vital foods and nutrients.

Current Research

In a study of 91 children aged four to nine years old, mild to severe intellectual developmental deficits were looked at for eating problems and sensory profile.

Findings from the study show significant correlations between sensory processing and eating problems at each SPD level. Most connections were found in those children with moderate to severe/profound levels [6].

Other studies on gastrointestinal (GI) issues show that those with ASD tend to have more GI symptoms, but further research shows that those with ASD seem to have difficulties in behavior and physical problems due to diet, and nutritional deficiencies [7].

Those with ASD often report gastrointestinal issues or digestion problems, to include stomach pain, diarrhea, constipation, acid reflux, vomiting, or bloating, which can also occur in those with eating disorders. Food allergies are also common in both disorders.

Those individuals with food selectivity issues are typically dealing with various environmental factors related to sensory modulation and regulation [8]. Selective eating can be defined as "eating very small amounts of food and/or restricting foods eaten to an extremely narrow selection of sometimes only one or two items [9]." This behavior can have significant developmental and health consequences. It can also increase the negative reaction to the introduction of new foods.

In conclusion, sensory processing disorders and eating disorders have a connection through picking eating, restricting eating and *Avoidant Restrictive Food Intake Disorder*, which falls under the eating disorder diagnosis. Both disorders include struggles with rigidity, sensory processing issues, negative associations with foods, and dysregulation of structure around mealtimes.

About the Author: Libby Lyons is a Licensed Clinical Social Worker and Certified Eating Disorder Specialist (CEDS). Libby has been practicing in the field of eating disorders, addictions, depression, anxiety and other comorbid issues in various agencies. Libby has previously worked as a contractor for the United States Air Force Domestic Violence Program, Saint Louis University Student Health and Counseling, Saint Louis Behavioral Medicine Institute Eating Disorders Program, and has been in Private Practice. Libby currently works as a counselor at Fontbonne University and is an adjunct professor at Saint Louis University, and is a contributing author for Addiction Hope and Eating Disorder Hope. Libby lives in the St. Louis area with her husband and two daughters. She enjoys spending time with her family, running, and watching movies.

References:

1. *http://www.foodandnutrition.org/September-October-2014/Picky-Eater-Sensory-Processing-Disorder/*

2. *https://www.brainbalancecenters.com/blog/2014/02/adhd-and-eating-disorders/*

3. *http://journals.sagepub.com/doi/abs/10.1177/0308022615586418?journalCode=bjod*

4. *https://www.hindawi.com/journals/aurt/2011/541926/*

5. *https://www.sensorysmarts.com/signs_of_spd.html*

6. *http://www.eatingdisordersonline.com/articles/science-and-research/what-is-sensory-processing-disorder*

7. *http://www.autismempowerment.org/understanding-autism/co-existing-conditions/*

8. *https://www.nationaleatingdisorders.org/sites/default/files/Toolkits/ParentToolkit.pdf*

9. *https://www.iidc.indiana.edu/pages/mealtime-and-children-on-the-autism-spectrum-beyond-picky-fussy-and-fads*
    Published on April 30, 2017. Reviewed By: Jacquelyn Ekern, MS, LPC on April 30, 2017. Published on *EatingDisorderHope.com*

Cleanse: Toxic Television
How Watching TV Leads to Weight Gain
By Suzanne Hiscock

Do you watch more than ten hours of TV a week? If you do, chances are you're overweight. Studies show a direct relationship between television watching and weight gain, especially in kids. According to Nielsen, the average American watches 35 hours of TV a week. That's only counting live TV!

On the flip side, the National Weight Control Registry (NWCR) says that 62% of the people they study watch less than ten hours a week. The NWCR tracks over 10,000 people who have lost and kept off a significant amount of weight.

That's 25 fewer hours spent watching TV than the average person. That's 72% less time spent watching TV.

Break the TV Habit and Lose a Pound a Week

Let's do a bit of math. What if the average American replaced those 25 hours with *walking 3 mph*?

A 150lb woman burns about 107 calories per hour sitting. That same woman would burn about 236 calories per hour walking at 3mph hour.

That's a difference of 129 extra calories burned per hour. Multiply that by 25, and you get an extra 3,225 calories burned.

That's almost a whole pound's worth of calories a week.

Other Ways Watching TV Can Lead to Weight Gain
It's not just the sitting around part of TV watching that adds to weight gain. Other factors come into play that can affect your weight, too.

- *Extra calories* – People tend to snack while watching TV, especially on *calorie-dense snack foods.*

- *Distraction* – According to Nielsen, 66% of American families eat dinner while watching TV. You can't listen to your *hunger cues* if you're listening to the boob tube.

- *Temptation* – Junk food and restaurant ads on TV tempt you into eating more and/or eating unhealthy foods.

- *Body Image* – The bodies you see on TV don't reflect real life. You'll see more thin people on TV and this can affect how you view yourself. And if you eat for comfort, you could end up eating more if you feel badly about yourself.

https://www.fitwatch.com/blog/how-watching-tv-leads-to-weight-gain

Cleanse: Snarknado

While the science on television "gossip" and weight loss is scant, the science correlating to social media and weight loss is vast.

"We are constantly bombarded by 'ideal' images in newspapers, magazines, on TV and especially online. Logically we know many of these images are teased and stretched, doctored and Photoshopped. Public image is all about lighting, angles and selection. But our subconscious mind remains gullible, and it can be a struggle not to compare those images to what we see in the mirror every day and end up feeling dissatisfied."

So many girls grow up into women who can't shake off the ideal image of 'thin as beautiful.' It's clearly not healthy. Psychologists know that internalizing a thin ideal leads to us becoming unhappy with ourselves and this can in turn generate unhelpful views toward food and eating, in particular dieting. For decades, newspapers and magazines were blamed for publishing pictures of rake-thin models perpetuating an impossibly skinny ideal. But you can multiply that exposure exponentially if you're a keen social media addict, spending hours each day flicking through perfection on your phone.

You might think you're just being nosy and voyeuristic as you scroll through a Kardashian Insta feed, or rush to catch up with Victoria Beckham, but this constant stream of unattainable (and very often airbrushed) beauty is definitely not good for your mental health. Social media makes it so hard to be happy with your body and your weight, and so hard to achieve a happy, healthy weight.

There's also the culture of photoshopped perfection that massively amplifies body dissatisfaction, in turn feeding the diet business. Bloggers rarely mention weight loss, but their ethos can sometimes hide a desire for thinness and sculpted, self-conscious beauty, all to be achieved seemingly without effort. This aspirational slenderness is hard to achieve and not really very different from the rejected old-fashioned diets of restriction.

It's not only women who feel and bend to this pressure. Men are of course also influenced by advertising – if they weren't then there wouldn't be such astronomical budgets for ad slots in sporting events. For men, however, an image of thinness is combined with muscle definition to create that difficult-to-achieve, six-pack ideal. Researchers at Harvard Medical School have identified a condition called 'muscle belittlement' whereby men think that they're less muscular than they really are. This distorted belief is thought to lie behind unhealthy eating patterns, *the use of performance-enhancing substances* (muscle-building supplements and even steroids), low self-esteem and, in extreme cases, depression.

Today, social media invades almost every aspect of our lives. It's no longer a young person's pastime – Instagram, Twitter, Facebook and Pinterest are compelling and compulsive essential accessories to almost every career and hobby. Yes, social media can bring joy and friendship.

But it can also be very destructive and frighteningly addictive. Studies now show that the more time you spend sharing, liking, tweeting and hash-tagging, the greater your risk of unhappiness is likely to be.

Too much exposure to social media, whether its old-fashioned celebrities or the new breed of foodie influencer, can distract from the real reasons to eat and what to eat. You might think you're in complete control, but the association between the beautiful, seemingly happy and perfect individuals on social media platforms with the food they are presenting can be utterly compelling. It can lead us to believe that if only we cooked and ate exactly what these Insta-celebs do, we too could be happy and life would be a breeze.

Social media food fads, which make food a fashion item, create yet another pressure on us. This elevates food way beyond its original status as a source of sustenance, and creates desire wrapped up in an ever-changing fashion buzz we struggle to keep up with. This can leave us feeling like we're never quite good enough, and this can progress to body dissatisfaction. *In some cases body dysmorphia* can result, if someone becomes so obsessive about areas of their body that they spend an inordinate amount of time worrying about perceived imperfections that no one else can even see.

That sense of competition with others to get the most friends, followers or likes, coupled with the temptation to derive self-worth from how many comments and shares your posts receive, could be breeding a dependence on external sources of validation that leaves us feeling bad about ourselves – think about that sinking feeling when no one acknowledges a post that you were hoping to get a huge response from. Social media can be isolating and, ironically, can make you feel disconnected and alone. These feelings can often result in *social anxiety*. Stress increases cortisol levels, which can result in weight loss for some. Ultimately, constantly comparing ourselves to airbrushed images leads to body dissatisfaction, which in turn is linked to overeating and/or cycles of eating and dieting.

And it isn't just about people. Glossy pictures of appetizing food or cooking have long been used by the advertising industry to tempt us to eat more, and such is the social media seduction that 'food porn' now even has its own searchable hashtag. If you choose to fill your social media feed with these delicious images, you might notice a change in your waistline – regularly viewing mouthwatering food photos on social media may trigger feelings of hunger and encourage overindulgence.

"Studies show that looking at pictures of food is enough to raise a person's levels of ghrelin, a hormone involved in the stimulation of hunger, as the appetizing image sends a rush of blood to the part of the brain responsible for taste, encouraging you to eat, even when you're not hungry. Researchers call this 'visual hunger' and it applies to cookery shows and flicking through recipe books. It certainly helps to explain why it's so hard to watch Bake Off without reaching for a biscuit or a slice of cake."

One important tenet of our method is to throw a lasso around your social media use and ask yourself whether everything on your social media feed is truly helpful. Be realistic and work out ways to trim some of the fat instead of following people or accounts that make you feel low or deprived, refresh your feed with inspirational sources that motivate you to exercise and offer deliciously healthy recipe ideas instead. Find and follow the sort of influencers more likely to make you feel strong and empowered, and choose to surround yourself with positive eating messages for the times when you are checking your phone.

At the end of the day, there's a lot to be said for taking regular social media breaks – you could even switch off completely for a while. *Whether you take a social media hiatus* or not, just remember that while it can seem like successful people just float effortlessly through life, never facing adversity or, if they do, responding like super-humans pushing through like some action-movie lead, Instagram feeds don't show the millions of little slip-ups, backtracking and diversions that make up real life for everyone. Social media is without a doubt the worst perpetuator of this, as we tend to only post the best bits of our lives in a polished and preened portrayal of human existence. It's not like that. Not at all.

Psychologist Dr. Meg Arroll specializes in health and the relationship between stress weight and fatigue, while health journalist Louise Atkinson has been writing about every diet under the sun for over 30 years. Both are clued up on the mental and physical implications of diets and weight loss, and teamed up to write to provide a science-based guide to identify emotional issues behind eating patterns and behavior around food, with practical techniques to help you to achieve a healthy weight and mindset long-term.

https://www.getthegloss.com/article/is-social-media-affecting-your-weight

Cleanse: The Friends You Keep and the Friend You Deep (Six)
The science on toxic relationships and weight loss.

The People Who Make You Fat
Who you're in contact with may determine the size of your belly
by *LAURA BEIL*
April 3, 2014
We've all known the friend in need who's no friend indeed. Or the relative who only speaks to you when it's time to complain. Or the coworker who is quick to dismiss your ideas. Maybe you're surrounded by them: the cranks, the users, the judgers, the blamers.

These toxic relationships may not just strain your patience or mental health. A new study that followed more than 3,000 adults in their 30s and 40s found that people saddled with burdensome "negative relationships" accumulated more belly fat over 15 years than those who didn't. To define "negative," the study volunteers were asked how often friends and family members made unfair demands, criticized, let them down, or just plain got on their nerves.

Previous studies have uncovered a link between poor social connections and obesity, but much of the data are just snapshots of one point in time and can't say which came first, says lead scientist Kiarri Kershaw, Ph.D., of Northwestern University. Relationships could sour because a person becomes obese, not the other way around. But Kershaw's research team tracked people over years, which gives a better sense of cause and effect.

In the American Journal of Epidemiology, the Northwestern researchers report that while everyone gained weight as they got older, the waistlines of people with stressful relationships ended up slightly larger overall. Doctors say fat that sits around your middle poses the greatest threat to the heart and diabetes risk.

Kershaw theorizes that one problem comes down to food. Strained relationships can cause stress, which may drive you to seek the comfort of junk food and alcohol, both of which add calories. Stress can also affect how your body metabolizes excess calories, says Briana Mezuk, Ph.D., of Virginia Commonwealth University, by triggering stress-response systems that make body fat more likely to end up in your abdomen. "Stress affects not just our emotions, but our biology," she says.

But there's good news, too. Just like bad connections might make you fat, healthy ones might keep you leaner. In the new study, people who reported more supportive relationships – relatives they can rely on, friends they can talk to – didn't gain as much belly fat as their peers. "Supportive relationships could be stress buffering, and keep you from using coping mechanisms like eating," says Kershaw. So if you find yourself in too much toxic company, consider whether your heart is worth the risk.

https://www.menshealth.com/weight-loss/a19532676/negative-relationships-and-your-waistline#:~:text=These%20toxic%20relationships%20may%20not,than%20those%20who%20didn%27t.

SuperFoods: I'll Take the Tchaikovsky
The science of classical music and weight loss.

Scientists all over the world agreed that music influences hormone production that are directly connected with our emotions. If you think about it you are influenced by music all the time. Think of your last time you watched a horror movie. Remember how music actually made your heart race faster. Music physicians in Japan and China help patients form their own music aid kits, where you can find CDs with the names like "Liver," "Lungs," "Migraine," or "Metabolism."

Now let me tell you about my most valuable discovery. Music can not only improve your overall health it can also help you lose weight! Eating dinner while listening to Mozart helps to improve your metabolism and food digestion. When you eat while listening to the pop or rock music you automatically start eating faster. As a result you swallow bigger pieces making it harder for your stomach to digest the food.

Exercising while listening to the classical music help you lose weight a lot faster than listening to loud fitness pop music. Why? Maybe because during the experiment a first group of people listening to Vivaldi music worked out on a stationary bike a half an hour longer than the group who was listening to the pop music.

Which inevitably leads to extra pounds. "When we listen to classical music, subconsciously you get an image of luxury, wealth and sophistication," explains this phenomenon psychology Dr. Adrian Nort. It improves our mood, and makes us take our time and eat slowly enjoying food.

https://www.boxingscene.com/weight-loss/17555.php#:~:text=Music%20can%20not%20only%20improve,your%20metabolism%20and%20food%20digestion.&text=Exercising%20while%20listening%20to%20the,to%20loud%20fitness%20pop%20music.

Can Classical Music Help to Reduce High Blood Pressure?
By Sagar Murli-
February 2, 2020
A recent study conducted on 120 participants, which was published in Deutsches Ärzteblatt International, showed a decrease in the systolic and diastolic pressures in individuals who listened to classical music. Patients in the study group listened to Mozart, Strauss and ABBA for 25 minutes, whereas

the control group did not listen to music. Participants who listened to ABBA amongst the three groups (Mozart, Strauss and ABBA) showed a minimal reduction in blood pressure. Researchers also suggested that the music should be without any lyrics, harmonizing and have few changes in rhythm to help lower blood pressure.[1]

Another study was conducted on 200 elderly people with hypertension in India to determine the effects of Indian classical music. Classical music enhances the intensity of neurotransmitters and induces pleasant feelings. Raga Malkauns, a serious, meditative raga that induces calmness was chosen from Hindustani classical music for this study. The participants were divided into two equal groups – the experimental and control groups. The control group was only on medications, whereas the experimental group listened to the raga for 15 minutes every evening for one month while on anti-hypertensive medications. Results from the experimental group showed a reduction in heart rate and mean arterial pressure as compared to the control group. A pleasant mood was also observed after music therapy.[2]

How music reduces blood pressure?

A study conducted by Taruna (2013) stated that the calming effect of music on the brain stimulates the production of nitrous oxide (NO), which works on blood vessels, thereby causing dilation of the blood vessels and further lowering the blood pressure.[3] However, the study conducted in India attributed this effect to the action of the parasympathetic nervous system.[4]

Other than helping improve blood pressure, music also has a considerable impact on lowering the respiration rate and the secretion of cortisol (a hormone released during stressful situations).[5]

Music can improve the physiological and psychological health of individuals and can help reduce mental and physical tension, anxiety, stress, depression and loneliness along with improving sleep quality and pain.[5]

Thus, it can be concluded that listening to classical music along with taking prescribed medicines are beneficial for patients with hypertension.

References:

1. World Health Organization. Hypertension [Internet]. [cited 2020 7 Jan]. Available from: https://www.who.int/news-room/fact-sheets/detail/hypertension.

2. Bustami. Relaxed music can reduce blood pressure in hypertension patients. Int J Sci Technol Res. 2018;7(4):171–3. Available from: *https://www.ijstr.org/final-print/apr2018/Relaxed-Music-Can-Reduce-Blood-Pressure-In-Hypertension-Patients.pdf*.

3. Loomba RS, Arora R, Shah PH, Chandrasekar S, Molnar J. Effects of music on systolic blood pressure, diastolic blood pressure, and heart rate: a meta-analysis. Indian Heart J. 2012 May–Jun;64(3):309–13. Available from: *https://www.ncbi.nlm.nih.gov/pmc/articles/P.M.C3860955/*.

4. *Trappe H, Voit, G. The cardiovascular effect of musical genres. 2016; 113:347–52. Available from: https://www.aerzteblatt.de/int/archive/article?id=179298.*

5. *Shankar VM, Geethanjali B, Veezhinathan M, Hariharakrishnan J, Balakrishnan N, Lakshmi L. Current Science. Forthcoming 2020. Available from: https://www.currentscience.ac.in/php/forthcoming/2019/33689.pdf.*

SuperFoods: Plating Plato

The only article I could find which speaks to reading and weight loss (other than those that deride weight loss literature as causing hunger by constantly describing the foods one cannot eat on a diet) involved a study of school age girls reading literature that reinforced positive body images showing slightly enhanced weight loss among those reading than those in the control group.

The study's experimental group included 31 obese girls aged 9 to 13, who were enrolled in the Healthy Lifestyles Program at Duke Children's Hospital, a comprehensive family-centered weight loss plan that addresses patients' medical, dietary and behavioral needs. The girls read a novel called 'Lake Rescue,' whose protagonist is an overweight preteen who struggles with low self-esteem, feelings of isolation and teasing because of her size. A group of 33 girls read a different book called Charlotte in Paris, which did not have an overweight heroine, and another group of 17 girls read neither book. At the end of the six-month intervention, all the girls who read books had lost weight, but the girls who read Lake Rescue lost more. They lowered their body mass index (BMI), a ratio of weight and height used to measure obesity, by .71, compared with .33 in the Charlotte group an average .05 increase among the nonreaders.

https://www.dailymail.co.uk/health/article-1069597/Reading-novel-help-obese-children-lose-weight.html#:~:text=Reading%20books%20can%20help%20children,their%20body%20mass%20index%20drop.

I did stumble upon this article which, though it does not address reading in general or classic literature in particular, does speak to placing one's mind in the best place for weight loss – a paradigm that lies at the heart of the Jailbird Diet.

How Daily Meditation Can Help You Lose Weight
Last Updated on Sep 9, 2019
By now, you've probably tried everything to shed off those pesky pounds, from restricting your calories to intensifying your workout routine. While these efforts might be helping you shed a pound or two every few weeks, there's something that can give you that extra boost: meditation.

This cost-free, natural, simple strategy can be very effective in helping you slim down, while also alleviating stress and anxiety. The research surrounding mindful meditation practices suggests that meditation is closely linked to weight loss.

The concepts of mindfulness and meditation can not only lower your stress levels and boost awareness. Having an attentive mind can keep you from binge eating and emotional eating. Because of this, meditation for weight loss can be a naturally healthy and effective way to lose weight and eat better.

About Meditation

Simply put, meditation is the act of focusing the attention on becoming more mindful. According to the American Meditation Society, during meditation, a person's attention essentially flows inward instead of engaging in the outer world of activity. The practice involves clearing the mind with the aim of returning to a state of calm emotions and straightforward thinking.

Some people practice meditation for only five minutes a day, though experts suggesting trying to work that up to about 20 minutes a day. For those who're just starting out, consider taking five minutes just after you wake up to clear your mind before getting on with your day.

Close your eyes and simply focus on your breathing pattern without trying to change it. If your mind wanders, which is quite common when starting out, just guide it back to your breathing.

Link Between Weight Loss and Meditation

Intention and Motivation

The main reason why meditation can be so effective in helping people lose weight is that it aligns the conscious and the unconscious mind into agreeing on the changes that you want to apply to your behaviors. These changes include regulating cravings for unhealthy foods, changing eating habits, and finding the motivation to exercise. It's therefore very important to have the mind involved in your weight loss journey because it's where the harmful, weight-gaining habits including emotional eating are entrenched. Meditation ideally helps you become more aware of these habits and thoughts, overcome them with time, and even replace them with positive, healthy habits.

Developing a meditation routine will also help you keep the idea of weight loss alive. It essentially brings the object to the forefront of your mind and your day. This way, it's much harder to forget, which it will motivate you to keep going.

Meditation creates a higher level of concentration and focuses on your weight loss goals. Since it's so easy to get distracted, taking some time out of your busy day to meditate will harbor that motivation.

Psychological Well-Being

Meditation and mindfulness have also been shown to improve psychological health. Mindfulness has been shown to lower emotional eating, binge eating, and generally enhance the weight loss process. Stress relief is one of the fastest benefits of meditation. It essentially takes you out of the fight-or-flight mode by lowering the levels of stress hormones in your body. Stress hormones such as cortisol usually signal the body to store more calories as fat. Because of this, high cortisol levels are going to make it much difficult for you to shed extra weight, even if you're consistently making healthy choices.

According to a study conducted by Carnegie Mellon University, all it takes is about 25 minutes of meditation three days in a row to reduce stress significantly.

1) *In another 2016 study, participants showed increased relaxation, attention, mind-body awareness, calmness, and even brain activity after completing a few short meditation sessions.*
2) *The study also stated that levels of self-control could increase with daily meditation practice.*
3) *Finally, in a recent research review, researchers evaluated that the role of meditation on weight loss, along with the behaviors that are often associated with poor eating.*
4) *They concluded that mindful meditation could be helpful in decreasing the frequency of binge-eating and emotional eating.*

Mindfulness

Although mindfulness is quite different from meditation, the two concepts go hand-in-hand. Meditation helps you let go of the future and past. Perhaps you have had a number of failed attempts at weight loss before or you're experiencing some anxieties about the future, such as getting rid of poor habits. Mindfulness while meditating lets you savor the present without fixating too much on these stressors.

Mindfulness and Meditation in Action

Meditation and mindfulness are known to improve psychological health. Mindfulness has been shown to lower emotional eating, binge eating, and generally enhancing weight loss.

Chronic stress is associated with a greater concentration of fats in the abdomen, especially through the overproduction of the stress hormone cortisol, which is also linked to higher mortality. Because of this link, a study from the University of California at San Francisco focused on identifying whether lowering stress levels through meditation can actually help lower the concentration of belly fat.

The study was published in 2011 in the Journal of Obesity and researched a group of 47 obese or overweight female participants (with an average of 31.2 bodies mass index), giving half of them a series of classes about mindfulness meditation techniques.

The classes involved coaching them on how to pay attention to sensations of food cravings, hunger, identify emotional eating triggers, learn self-acceptance, and become aware of negative emotions. The guided meditations were provided to introduce new mindful eating skills, such as paying a close attention to the taste of food as well as eating more slowly than usual.

In general, the study group received nine classes, each lasting two and a half hours, along with a silent retreat day where they were encouraged to practice their new mindful eating and meditation skills. They were also encouraged to use the mindful skills when they got home in assignments of up to 30 minutes per day during or before meals, six days a week, and to log in their meditation activity.

Both the control groups and the study group received also received a two-hour nutrition and exercise information session. At the end of the research period, all of the participants were measured for their distribution and amount of abdominal fat, along with their cortisol levels.

Two key outcomes of the study were evaluated: whether the stress reduction and mindful eating program reduced emotional eating and whether it affected the amount of belly fat in participants.

In general, the study found these practiced decreased emotional eating, reduced stress levels, increased awareness of their bodily sensations, and reduced food cravings.

Additionally, blood cortisol levels were lower in the treatment group compared to the control group. Moreover, participants who experienced the most significant improvements in their mindful eating generally had a greater awareness of their hunger sensations, were more successful at reducing their chronic stress and experienced the greatest reduction in abdominal fat – by more than 500 grams in just the 4-month period.

The researchers assert that mindful meditation training in human beings can help people struggling with weight loss to cope better with stress and the rest of their negative emotions. That's because reduced stressed can promote a better body fat distribution from relaxing more and eating healthier.

Conclusion

No meditation practice for weight loss can help you lose weight without changing to a healthy diet and activity plan. The bottom line when trying to lose weight often involves creating a calorie deficit. Nonetheless, a program of mindful awareness is more likely to go a long way in making the process easier, and may even help you keep off the weight for good. Plus, meditation promises to give your health a big boost and shed some weight off you without costing you a cent.

https://monq.com/eo/meditation/daily-meditation-weight-loss/
By Jesse Waddell

SuperFoods: Cross-Wording
BY MARKHA.M. HEID
SEPTEMBER 19, 2018

I have attached here an article discussing brain activity and weight loss more for the amusement of calculating how much more calories you burn cross-wording while watching TV than by just watching TV alone. Perhaps this will incentivize your cross-wording if the broader implications I try to draw between cross-wording and weight loss do not.

You spent Sunday on the couch, skimming your social feeds and watching HGTV. Monday at work was a different story; your job involves creative problem solving and other difficult mental activities. Does the extra brainpower you use at work burn more energy than your Sunday spent watching Fixer Upper reruns? "The basic answer is yes," says Ewan McNay, an associate professor of psychology and behavioral neuroscience at the University of Albany.

The brain – unlike any other part of the body – runs exclusively on the sugar glucose, and strenuous cognitive activities require more glucose than simple ones, says McNay, who has studied how the brain uses energy to perform work. During a difficult memorization task, for example, the parts of your brain involved in memory formation will start consuming more energy, but other brain areas will show no such increase. "You will in fact burn more energy during an intense cognitive task than you would vegging out watching Oprah or whatever," he says. But in the context of the average person's overall energy expenditure, the difference in calorie burn from one mental task to another is a tiny amount, he adds.

To put cranial calorie burn in perspective, it helps to understand how your body burns energy. Unless you're a professional athlete, most of the energy your body uses doesn't have much to do with movement or exercise. A good-sized chunk – roughly 8% to 15% – goes toward digesting the stuff you swallow, while a much larger portion is required to power your organs and keep you alive and functioning. And no part of you demands more energy than your brain.

"As an energy-consumer, the brain is the most expensive organ we carry around with us," says Dr. Marcus Raichle, a distinguished professor of medicine at Washington University School of Medicine in St. Louis. While the brain represents just 2% of a person's total body weight, it accounts for 20%

of the body's energy use, Raichle's research has found. That means during a typical day, a person uses about 320 calories just to think.

Different mental states and tasks can subtly affect the way the brain consumes energy. "If we were to put you in a scanner and we looked at what's going on [in your brain] while in front of the TV or doing a crossword, your brain's activity would change if we gave you a demanding task, and it would use more energy," he says. But if you're hoping to think yourself slim, Raichle says you're out of luck. While the brain burns a lot of energy, any changes in brain activity and energy use during a tough mental task are minute: "maybe a 5% change against the backdrop of all brain activity," he says. Even if you were to keep your brain immersed in difficult mental pursuits all day long, this 5% change wouldn't add up to much. "Calorie-wise it would be very modest," Raichle says, adding that you would expend more energy pacing back and forth.

The bulk of your brain's energy consumption is put toward sustaining your alertness, monitoring your environment for important information, and managing other "intrinsic" activities. In terms of its energy demands, "an individual thought is cheap, but the machinery that makes it cheap is very expensive," he adds.

McNay agrees that our brains don't expend a whole lot more energy during tough tasks than during simple ones. A person doing cognitively challenging work for eight hours would burn about 100 more calories than a person watching TV or daydreaming for the same amount of time, he estimates. "If you were doing something really demanding that uses multiple senses – something like learning to play an instrument – that might get as high as 200 [calories]," he says. "But we're talking eight hours of learning a new instrument."

Even in this hypothetical instrument-learning session, the brain's ability to stay on task would taper off as its stores of glucose dwindle. "You'd run into this depletion effect where you can't sustain the same level of cognitive performance," he says. Drinking Gatorade or gobbling a few jelly beans could replenish your glucose stores and help restore your brain to full power. But the calories in those foods would easily outnumber any you'd burn.

However, there could still be a calorie-burning upshot for people who spend their days performing mentally challenging work. Even if you're only burning a small number of extra calories each day, that could, theoretically, add up to something meaningful over a period of 50 or 60 years, McNay says – so thinking things through is worth it.

Feeding Time at the Zoo

The type of intermittent fasting produced by the BOP kitchen schedule seems to have become a trending weight loss technique since I went away. The theory behind the success of such fasting is summed up in the following article:

By Jenae Sitzes and Marygrace Taylor for prevention.com, July 2, 2019.

One of the most popular types of intermittent fasting is called the 16:8 diet, where you limit your food intake to an 8-hour eating window and go 16 hours without eating any food. Some people call it the 16:8 diet or 16:8 fasting. Here's what you should know about it – and whether it can really help you lose weight.

What is the 16:8 diet?

The 16:8 diet is a version of intermittent fasting that restricts eating to an 8-hour window. During that time, you're allowed to eat and drink what you want with no calorie restrictions. During the 16-hour fasting period, you can (and should) drink plenty of water. Black coffee and tea are fine, too.

What time period works best? Keeping your eating window earlier – say, from 7 A.M. to 3 P.M. – seems to be the most beneficial. The body's biological clock is primed to eat earlier in the day, explains Courtney Peterson, PhD, assistant professor of nutrition at the University of Alabama at Birmingham. "In most people, blood sugar control is best in the morning and gets worse as the day progresses. You also digest food faster in the morning. So there's a metabolic advantage to eating earlier in the daytime," she says.

But if that timeframe seems unrealistic, don't worry. Recent findings suggest that bumping your eating window just a little bit later, from 10 A.M. to 6 P.M., could also be effective for weight loss. When following the 16:8 diet, you restrict eating to an 8-hour window and then do a 16-hour fast.

Can the 16:8 diet help you lose weight?

It might. When 23 obese adults restricted their eating from 10 A.M. to 6 P.M. for 12 weeks, they ate around 350 fewer calories per day compared to the control group, according to a recent Nutrition and Healthy Aging study. They also lost a few pounds and saw a drop in their systolic blood pressure (the top number). However, that study was very small, and more research will be needed to confirm the results. Going for longish periods without eating seems to send the body into fat-burning mode and limit blood sugar spikes. "Those two factors combined mean that you're reducing the blood sugar highs and lows that make you hungrier," Peterson says. Time-restricted eating also keeps your appetite in check by lowering the hunger hormone ghrelin, she adds.

There's another reason why 16:8 dieters might end up eating less. "I think participants found it difficult to eat all of their regular meals and snacks within the 8-hour timeframe," says Kristina Varady, PhD, associate professor of nutrition at the University of Illinois Chicago and a co-author of the Nutrition and Healthy Aging study. If trying to eat breakfast, lunch, and dinner between 10 A.M. and 6 P.M. seems like a squeeze, you'll likely end up cutting out a meal or shrinking your portions.

What are the drawbacks of following the 16:8 diet?

While the 16:8 diet seems like a great way to drop weight fast, it does have some cons. Sarah Mirkin, RD, author of Fill Your Plate, Lose the Weight, a 21-day meal plan designed to help women over 40 lose weight, says, "I think that it limits food intake to such a small window of time that it's difficult for someone to meet their nutritional needs."

Indeed, fasting for a long period of time probably means you're not able to enjoy three full meals with snacks each day. Whether you're skipping breakfast or dinner, missing a meal always results in not receiving adequate nutrients. And since the 16:8 diet gives you license to eat whatever you want, you might be tempted to fill up only on fatty, processed foods, especially if you're feeling ravenous. Hunger can also clout your better judgment and lead you to binge eat as well. "Studies show that the majority of people are not able to sustain it for very long and oftentimes end up binging on unhealthy foods, causing weight gain," Mirkin says. Other drawbacks of 16:8 fasting include poor sleep, muscle mass loss (since it doesn't allow enough time during the day to meet protein needs), disordered/binge eating, weakness, nausea, and fatigue, Mirkin says.

To help you make better food choices and avoid binge eating, Mirkin recommends sticking to a 12-hour eating window instead of an 8-hour one. "This allows adequate sleep and prevents late-night munching. It also allows you to fuel evenly throughout the day so that a person is able to meet their nutritional needs without watching the clock so closely," Mirkin explains.

Professor Mead

There is some diet literature that suggests that the food memory is a link to weight loss. If there is a causal link between one's ability to remember and visualize meals throughout the day – if such memory creates a trigger to eat less in subsequent meals – than this may be the science the helps us understand why Professor Mead is so important to the weight loss process. Here is an article that explains the relationship between daily food memory and weight loss:

How To Curb Hunger Pangs with Your Mind
By David Robson, *21st January 2015*
BBC.com

There may be a simple way to lose weight using only the power of thought. You just have to know how, says David Robson.

Eric Robinson has a surprising tool for weight loss. It's something we all have, but perhaps don't use it as much as we'd like: our memory.

Dieters often feel that they are waging war with their stomachs, but psychologists like Robinson believe that appetite is formed as much in the mind as our guts. So much so that if you try to remember the last food you've eaten, thinks Robinson, you can get thinner without the hunger pangs.

"Lots of research has now shown that subtle psychological factors can impact how much you eat – but people still aren't aware of the influence," he says. "And that's important, given the worldwide obesity problem." If this is true, how could it work?

The inspiration for this latest thinking comes, in part, from people with very poor memories, suffering from a deficit known as anterograde amnesia. You could meet these people and have a deep, involved conversation – but after 20 minutes they wouldn't have the faintest idea who you were. "Something happens to them, but you come back 20 minutes later and they have no recollection of it," says Robinson, who is based at the University of Liverpool.

The same is true of the food they eat. One of the key studies involved a former musician and a former banker, both of whom had developed anterograde amnesia after a herpes infection damaged parts of the temporal cortex, the part of the brain that lays down new memories. They were first given a plate of sandwiches and cake, which they ate until they were full. The *plates were taken away – only to be returned with more helpings 15 minutes later. While healthy volunteers would tend to feel too full to eat more, **the two amnesic subjects happily filled themselves a second time**. "They forget they've had their last meal, and so if they are offered another one, they'll eat that too," says Glyn Humphreys, at the University of Oxford, who conducted the study.*

Despite their poor memories, the amnesic pair weren't completely oblivious to what they had just eaten. In another part of the experiment, they were allowed to taste a range of foods – rice pudding, crisps, or chocolate, asked to wait a bit, and then offered the plates again. Most people, like you or I, seek a variety of flavors, so we change our preference a second time round – a phenomenon called "sensory specific satiety." Like us, the two amnesic volunteers also felt less tempted by their previous choice – even though they said they had no recollection of having eaten it. Their changing preference suggests they didn't have a problem with the sensory processing of the dishes – it's just they couldn't form an explicit, conscious memory of the meal. And without that recollection, they still felt hungry, even when their stomachs were full.

*You might suspect that a healthy brain is smart enough to take notice of what you've eaten, but recent research shows it is easily fooled. Consider this **ingenious experiment** by Jeff Brunstrom at the University of Bristol. His subjects thought their task was simple: to eat a bowl of soup. Unbeknown to them, Brunstrom had hooked up a pipe that passed through the table and into the bowl, which allowed him to top-up some of his subjects' soup without them noticing. He found that their later snacking depended almost entirely on the appearance of the bowl at the start of the meal – whether it seemed big or small – and very little on the actual amount he had fed them. All of which weakens the common notion that hunger is governed solely by the hormones from the gut. "I'm not suggesting that kind of signaling isn't important, but the role of cognition has been under represented," says Brunstrom. And in some circumstances, it may be more important.*

*That could easily have an impact in our hectic, modern lives. Working lunches are now commonplace in most offices, and many people watch TV or play with their smartphones and laptops during evening meals. All of these distractions might affect your memories of what you've eaten. Brunstrom, for instance, asked subjects to eat with one hand while **they played solitaire with*** *the other. Thanks to the distraction, they struggled to recall the meal, and pigged out on more biscuits later in the day.*

It is for this reason that the researchers are now looking into ways of boosting the sensory memory of food. Robinson recently tested whether a recording, played during a meal, could help a group of obese women to eat some ham sandwiches more mindfully. The instructions were simple: the 3-minute clip asked them to focus on the full sensual experience of the meal – the sights, the taste, and the smell. A second control group ate with the pleasant sound of a cuckoo's melodious calls. As Robinson had hoped, the people asked to savor their food gave fuller descriptions later on, and snacked less three hours later – consuming 30% fewer calories.

*The approach may not work for everyone, but Robinson has other ideas for alternative techniques; in another experiment, asking people to consciously remember what they had eaten earlier in the day seemed to discourage over-eating later on. Your imagination may even offer a helping hand: a team in Pennsylvania has found that visualizing your cravings, in full detail, seems to trick the mind into thinking it has actually eaten the snack – **reducing desire and actual consumption**.*

***Robinson is currently working on an app** that could remind someone to recall their previous meals throughout their daily routine. But despite all these efforts, he points out that we still need bigger clinical trials to test if memory tricks are really effective in the ongoing battle with obesity. He's also concerned that people might find the procedures tiresome – particularly if they have to listen to a recording every time they eat.*

Promisingly, "attentive eating" does not seem to reduce his subjects' pleasure of their meals; on the contrary, they actually seemed to find it more enjoyable to absorb themselves in the sea of flavors hitting their tongues. "It's not unimaginable that savoring food could actually be a good thing."

If they work, these memory tricks could therefore offer that rare thing: a slimming program that actually enhances your pleasure in food. And surely that would be one of the more palatable solutions to the fight against obesity.

Miles To Go before I Sleep
The science of walking and weight loss:

How Walking Can Help You Lose Weight and Belly Fat
https://www.healthline.com/nutrition/walking-for-weight-loss
If you want to stay fit and healthy, it's important to exercise regularly.

This is because being physically active reduces your risk of developing health conditions like heart disease, diabetes and cancer. In addition to helping you live a longer and healthier life; exercise can also be beneficial for weight loss and maintenance. In fact, walking isn't just good for you – it's one of the easiest forms of exercise to incorporate into your day-to-day life.

This article explores how walking more often can help you lose weight and belly fat.

Walking Burns Calories

Your body needs energy (in the form of calories) for all the complex chemical reactions that allow you to move, breathe, think and function normally. However, daily calorie needs vary from person to person and are affected by things like your weight, sex, genes and activity level.

It's well known that you need to burn more calories than you consume to lose weight.

Furthermore, people who are more physically active burn more calories

However, modern living and work environments may mean that you spend large parts of your day sitting, especially if you have an office job. Unfortunately, a sedentary lifestyle can not only contribute to weight gain it can also increase your risk of health problems. Trying to get more exercise by walking more often can help you burn more calories and reduce these risks. In fact, walking a mile (1.6 km) burns approximately 100 calories, depending on your sex and weight.

One study measured the number of calories burned by non-athletes who walked at a brisk pace of 3.2 miles (5 km) per hour or ran at a pace of 6 mph for about a mile. It found those who walked at a brisk pace burned an average of 90 calories per mile. Furthermore, although running burned significantly more calories, it only burned around 23 more calories per mile, on average, meaning both forms of exercise contributed significantly to the number of calories burned. To increase the intensity of your walk and burn even more calories, try walking on routes with hills or slight inclines.

It Helps Preserve Lean Muscle

When people cut calories and lose weight, they often lose some muscle in addition to body fat.

This can be counterproductive, as muscle is more metabolically active than fat. This means it helps you burn more calories each day. Exercise, including walking, can help counter this effect by preserving lean muscle when you lose weight. This can help reduce the drop-in metabolic rate that often occurs with weight loss, making your results easier to maintain. What's more, it can reduce age-related muscle loss, helping you retain more of your muscle strength and function.

Walking Burns Belly Fat

Storing a lot of fat around your midsection has been linked to an increased risk of diseases like type two diabetes and heart disease. In fact, men with a waist circumference greater than 40 inches (102 cm) and women with a waist circumference greater than 35 inches (88 cm) have abdominal obesity, which is considered a health risk.

One of the most effective ways to reduce belly fat is to regularly take part in aerobic exercise, such as walking. In one small study, obese women who walked for 50–70 minutes three times per week for 12 weeks, on average, reduced their waist circumference by 1.1 inches (2.8 cm) and lost 1.5% of their body fat. Another study found that people on a calorie-controlled diet who walked for one hour five times per week for 12 weeks lost an extra 1.5 inches (3.7 cm) off their waistlines and 1.3% more body fat, compared to those who followed the diet alone. Other studies on the effects of walking briskly for 30– 60 minutes per day have observed similar results.

It Improves Your Mood

Exercise is known to boost your mood.

In fact, physical activity has been shown to improve your mood and decrease feelings of stress, depression and anxiety. It does this by making your brain more sensitive to the hormones serotonin and norepinephrine. These hormones relieve feelings of depression and stimulate the release of endorphins, which make you feel happy. This is a great benefit in itself. However, experiencing an improvement in mood when you walk regularly might also make the habit easier to keep up with.

What's more, some studies have found that if you enjoy a physical activity, it can increase the likelihood that you will continue to do it. People tend to exercise less if they don't enjoy it, which can be a result of the exercise being too physically demanding This makes walking an excellent choice, as it's a moderate-intensity exercise. That's likely to motivate you to walk more, rather than give up.

Walking Can Help You Keep Weight Off

Many people who lose weight end up gaining it all back

However, regular exercise plays an important role in helping you maintain weight loss.

Regular exercise like walking does not only help increase the amount of energy you burn day-to-day but it also helps you build more lean muscle so that you burn more calories, even at rest. Furthermore, participating in regular, moderate-intensity exercise like walking can improve your mood, making you more likely to stay active in the short-term.

A recent review estimated that to maintain a stable weight, you should walk at least 150 minutes per week However, if you've lost a lot of weight, you may need to exercise more than 200 minutes per week to prevent yourself from regaining it. In fact, studies have found that people who exercise the most are usually the most successful at maintaining their weight loss, whereas people who exercise the least are likely to regain the weight.

Incorporating more walking into your day can help you increase the amount of exercise you and contribute toward your daily activity goals.

Food Logs

"Instead of three meals a day, if it be necessary, eat one; instead of a hundred dishes, five, and reduce other things in proportion."
   Walden p. 239

My daily log consisted of three components: (1) weight recorded first thing in the morning; (2) laps/miles completed and the time of completion; (3) food consumed at each meal. Any short-term weight loss program that does not record these elements on a daily basis is more aspirational than executable. Recording the weight triggers guilt and exultation – emotions equally powerful in driving you to goal; the laps and meals provide the checkpoints along the way – guideposts to reconfigure your weight loss plan should you hit the wall, which you invariably will over a month's long journey.

To give you a sense of the kind of eating that supports a 100-pound weight loss program, I will take you through some of the food logs that tracked my greatest weight loss period (5 pounds lost per week in weeks 5, 6, and 7) and those that tracked the period when I hit the wall (one pound gained and one pound lost in weeks 25 and 26).

Week 5: July 24 – August 1, 2019
Wednesday 7.24:
Breakfast: Raisin Bran + one 1/2-pint skim milk
Lunch: Burger Patty – 1.6 oz. burger
              Clam Pouch – 3 oz. baby minced clams
Dinner: Meat, Clam, Dressing/Salad

The meat was, most likely meat sauce – a classic inextricable protein – which in the first months I would eat then rejected outright as I felt there was too much sugar in the recipe.

This was the first week that I put clam into meals; my guess is that I was pleasantly surprised at lunch with the clams so much so that I replicated this approach at dinner.

Thursday 7.25:

Breakfast: Raisin Bran + one 1/2-pint skim milk

Lunch: Chicken Quarter (drumstick and thigh)

Dinner: Not recorded. This did happen thought it was rare.

Friday 7.26:

Breakfast: Raisin Bran + one 1/2-pint skim milk

Lunch: Three "crab patties" – more like small hockey pucks of haddock and filler

Dinner: Chicken Quarter (drumstick and thigh), peas, carrots, rice, 3 bites of ice cream.

This marks the first introduction of chicken quarter outside Thursday lunch (*see Chapter 21. Do The Hustle*).

This is also the first recorded appearance of ice cream – the most high value food product coming out of the kitchen. The brand was Pierre's, the flavor was MooseTracks. The three bites represented my extracting the peanut butter chocolate chunks and ditching the vanilla ice cream.

Saturday 7.27:

Breakfast: Raisin Bran + one 1/2-pint skim milk

Lunch: Eggs + turkey bacon

Dinner: Chicken Quarter (drumstick and thigh)

On Saturdays and Sundays, breakfast had its own line consisting of oatmeal or grits, pastry, and a piece of fruit. This was served between 7:30 and 8:00. It did not alter my breakfast cereal though I would usually take a bite of the pastry (and not record) and take the fruit (usually a banana) for consumption later that day or week.

The eggs at weekend lunch were either scrambled (think the quality of a Hampton Inn buffet) or hard boiled – another high valued food product for the protein it delivered to the lifters.

Sunday 7.28:

Breakfast: Raisin Bran + one 1/2-pint skim milk
Lunch: Eggs + bacon (pork)
Dinner: Not recorded

Monday 7.29:
Breakfast: Raisin Bran + one 1/2-pint skim milk
Lunch: 2 tuna packs + cheese + 3 bites ice cream
Dinner: Chicken = mayo + fried rice

Five weeks in and I had yet to make the transition from tuna to mackerel; a change I would make the next month and never look back. The dinner reflects an extractable with benefits meal where I am removing the chicken from the fried rice, mixing it with mayo for chicken salad, then taking a few bites of the fried rice for my side.

Tuesday, 7.29:
Breakfast: Raisin Bran + one 1/2-pint skim milk
Lunch: Chicken Patty + 3 bites of cake
Dinner: Sausage + orange

I would peel the breading away from the chicken as best I could at lunch. The sausage was a pork link the size of a large hot dog. The orange was, most likely, a holdover from the breakfast bags. Food service would, at times, put fruit out by the water/juice station but generally apples, never oranges or bananas. Can you guess why fruit is never placed out for self-serve in a higher security prison? Answer: Hooch. The BOP knew that prisoners will take the fruit sugar and ferment it into an alcohol (Or so I am told).

Week 6 August 1 – August 7, 2019
Thursday 8.1:
Breakfast: Raisin Bran + one 1/2-pint skim milk
Lunch: Chicken Quarter (drumstick and thigh) + salad
Dinner: 2 turkey dogs + Chicken Quarter + cole slaw.

Again, I was distributing at dinner proceeds (the drumstick) from my work in food service (See Part IX, Chapter 21, Do The Hustle).

Friday 8.2:
Breakfast: Raisin Bran + one 1/2-pint skim milk

Lunch: Fish cake + soup + clams + cantaloupe
Dinner: Unrecorded

Saturday 8.3:
Breakfast: Raisin Bran + one 1/2-pint skim milk
Lunch: Clams + peanut butter
Dinner: Chicken Quarter

I would routinely miss Saturday and Sunday chow line as these were the only visiting days at the camp and I would be at visits in the morning from 8:30 till 11:15 and afternoons from 1:00 till 3:00. That is why lunch and dinner were either commissary based (clams/peanut butter) or food hustle based (chicken quarter).

Sunday 8.4:
Breakfast: Raisin Bran + one 1/2-pint skim milk
Lunch: Chicken quarter + cheese
Dinner: Clams + salad + dressing + 2 bites of cake

Some Sunday dinners, food service would put out for self-serve left over cake from breakfast.

Monday 8.5:
Breakfast: Raisin Bran + one 1/2-pint skim milk
Lunch: Baked potato skin + cheese
Dinner: Chicken + Russian dressing

Again, an extractable with benefits dinner only this time, instead of using my commissary mayo, I used the food service Russian dressing to make chicken salad.

Tuesday 8.6:
Breakfast: Raisin Bran + one 1/2-pint skim milk
Lunch: Pastrami + mayo + 2 bites ice cream
Dinner: Pork + potato + pear

Pastrami was rarely served and not exactly what I would get at my go to Jewish deli back home, Hymies of Merion, PA, but it was still pastrami and not to be passed up. The pork at dinner was a small pork chop which I would eat sometime with mayo and sometimes without.

Wednesday, 8.7:

Breakfast: Raisin Bran + one 1/2-pint skim milk

Lunch: Burger + 1 piece pastrami + dressing

Dinner: Turkey + salad + dressing

At lunch I was carrying over the pastrami from the previous lunch to supplement the junior-sized burger. The dinner was called chef salad which comprised a small Styrofoam bowl of turkey and a tray of chopped salad and self-serve dressing.

A couple observations on these weeks of eating of my greatest weight loss before we move to the weeks of eating at my slowest weight loss.

I am still less than two months into my journey and adhering pretty much to the food service menus. While I have started to add food hustle protein into the mix and redistribute protein from one day to another, I am consuming almost entirely what is being served. The only exception is the bringing in of clams and peanut butter when I am not physically present for the chow line.

While I never counted calories, a review of these meals presents a daily calorie count I would guess now to be between 1,500 and 1,800 calories per day distributed as follows: breakfast – 300 calories; lunch – 750 calories; dinner – 750 calories. Adding snacks, which I will discuss later, would increase the daily calorie count by 250 for a total of 2050.

On healthline.com, there is a tool that analyzes the number of calories per day required to lose weight. Enter your height, weight, age, gender and activity level, and they will give you the calories count necessary to maintain, lose or lose fast. Entering my numbers for Week 5 and 6 of my journey generates the following results:

To maintain weight: 3,729

To lose weight: 2,983

To lose weight fast: 2,237

By healthline.com's analysis, I was consuming a low enough calorie count per day to lose weight fast which was exactly what I was doing in these weeks of the journey. But I was not starving myself. When cake and ice cream were served, I ate it, though not the entire portion. I didn't take the skin of the baked chicken, I savored it. Mayo and salad dressing I would use liberally. But what you rarely if ever see in these weeks is starch or bread – rice, potatoes, beans, bread were almost non-existent in my diet. As you can also see, vegetables (aside from salad) were, unfortunately, almost non-existent as well.

And how did this change, if at all, during the weeks I hit the wall. Let's see.

Week 25; January 22 – January 28, 2020 (+ 1 pound)
Wednesday, 1.22:
Breakfast: Raisin Bran + one 1/2-pint skim milk
Lunch: Burger + 1 slice cheese
Dinner: Burger + cheese + salad + bread (1 slice)

Thursday 1.23:
Breakfast: Raisin Bran + one 1/2-pint skim milk
Lunch: Chicken Quarter (drumstick and thigh)
Dinner: 2 turkey dogs + cheese + Granny Smith apple

Friday 1.24:
Breakfast: Raisin Bran + one 1/2-pint skim milk
Lunch: Mackerel + mayo
Dinner: Unrecorded

Saturday 1.25:
Breakfast: Raisin Bran + one 1/2-pint skim milk
Lunch: Pastrami + cheese
Dinner: Sausage + ice cream
If I did not record the number of bites of ice cream, it means I ate the entire serving.

Sunday 1.26:
Breakfast: Raisin Bran + one 1/2-pint skim milk
Lunch: Chicken quarter
Dinner: Nell's White Clam Pizza
As the food hustle chicken leg was handed out on Thursday and left in my locker till consumed, Sunday was pushing its shelf-life limit. I stopped the practice of holding onto the chicken more than 48 hours and would definitely

237

not recommend holding in an un-refrigerated space for more than 24 hours anywhere other than prison.

Monday 1.27:

Breakfast: Raisin Bran + one 1/2-pint skim milk

Lunch: Sausage + cheese

Dinner: 2 sausage rounds + 2 hard-boiled eggs + mayo

Both lunch and dinner are a redistribution of the Sunday lunch sausage and hard-boiled eggs.

Tuesday, 1.28:

Breakfast: Raisin Bran + one 1/2-pint skim milk

Lunch: Hard boiled eggs + turkey bacon + cheese

Dinner: 4 round sausage + 1 long sausage + 2 cheese

Again, I am redistributing weekend protein later into the week as the round sausages and hard-boiled eggs were staples of Saturday and Sunday lunches.

The recording of cheese throughout the week signals the introduction of a new part of my food hustle described later on. Cheese slices were rarely served on chow line.

Week 26; January 29 – February 3, 2020 (-1 pound)

Wednesday, 1.29:

Breakfast: Raisin Bran + one 1/2-pint skim milk

Lunch: Sausage soup

Dinner: Sausage soup

Thursday 1.30:

Breakfast: Raisin Bran + one 1/2-pint skim milk

Lunch: Chicken Quarter (drumstick and thigh)

Dinner: Burger (from Wed lunch) + Cheesesteak

Cheesesteak was very similar to the Steakum brand which I loved as a teenager.

Friday 1.31:

Breakfast: Raisin Bran + one 1/2-pint skim milk

Lunch: Unrecorded

Dinner: Turkey, cheese, hardboiled egg, mayo

The dinner was Chef Salad: turkey in the Styrofoam container, shredded cheese, and the egg.

Saturday 2.1:

Breakfast: Raisin Bran + one 1/2-pint skim milk

Lunch: Bacon + cheese

Dinner: Chicken Quarter + Chino fried rice ice

One of the few times I ate an entire portion of fried rice. I did so because Chino made it with his hot chili oil which I loved so much, I purchased minced garlic from commissary to give to him to prepare it.

Sunday 2.2:

Breakfast: Raisin Bran + one 1/2-pint skim milk

Lunch: Chicken wings + pizza top

Dinner: Murder Mike's Stromboli

This was Super Bowl Sunday which was one of the days the BOP Food Service splurged. Chicken wings were a real treat – only served on chow line this one time. Pizza top means just that – I ate the cheese off the top of the slices and discarded the dough and crust.

Monday 2.3:

Breakfast: Raisin Bran + one 1/2-pint skim milk

Lunch: Lettuce + cheese + corn + dressing

Dinner: Clams + cheese + meatballs and mayo + jalapeño

I had purchased jalapeño from commissary.

Tuesday, 2.04:

Breakfast: Raisin Bran + one 1/2-pint skim milk

Lunch: 2 meatballs + 2 cheese slices + carrots + pear

Dinner: pepper steak + veggies + turkey burger

Printed in the USA
CPSIA information can be obtained
at www.ICGtesting.com
LVHW011059280723
753395LV00005B/77